Best of Totto-chan:
The Little Girl at the Window

To the memory of Sosaku Kobayashi
この本を、亡き、小林宗作先生に捧げます。

装幀 ● 菊地信義
装画 ● いわさきちひろ

Published by Kodansha International Ltd., 17-14, Otowa 1-chome, Bunkyo-ku, Tokyo 112.
Originally published in 1981, in Japanese, under the title *Madogiwa no Totto-chan* by Kodansha Ltd., Tokyo.

First edition, 1996

ISBN 4-7700-2127-5
96 97 98 99 10 9 8 7 6 5 4 3 2 1

ベスト・オブ

窓ぎわのトットちゃん

Best of Totto-chan: The Little Girl at the Window

黒柳徹子［著］
ドロシー・ブリトン［訳］
いわさきちひろ［絵］

Bilingual Books

刊行のことば

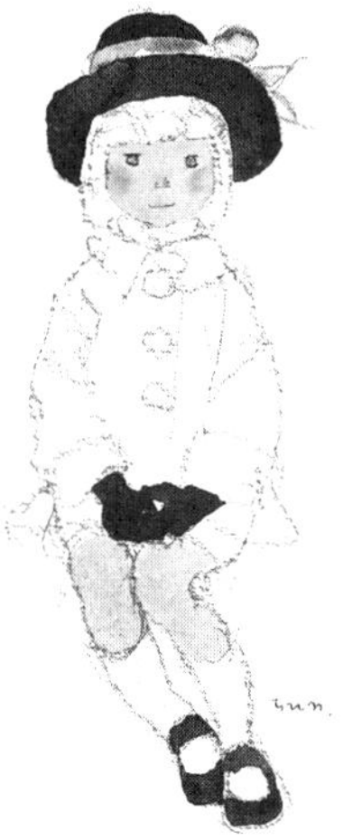

黒柳徹子さんの『窓ぎわのトットちゃん』(1981年に講談社より刊行)は、子供からお年寄りまで、男女差も年齢差も越えて、これまで700万人の心をとらえつづけた空前のベストセラーです。

そこで小社は、〝あの感動〟を再び味わっていただきたく『窓ぎわのトットちゃん』61編の中から30編を集めてバイリンガル・ブックにしました。

社会ー家族ー子供という日常の身近な関係の意味が問われている今日、素朴で無邪気な笑い声に満ちた幸福なリトル・コスモスが現にあったことを思い起こしてください。そして、勇気と愛が……、国境も民族の違いも越えて世界に届きますように。

また、この対訳本は、日本語と英語を読み比べる楽しみも味わうことができます。生き生きした‘話し言葉’が充満している『窓ぎわのトットちゃん』は、「やさしい使える英語表現」が学べるテキストブックにもなることでしょう。

いわさきちひろさんの挿絵を豊富に掲載しました。文章とみごとにマッチした絵は、「トットちゃん」をより生き生きと躍動させています。英語でも日本語でもあなたの読みたい方でかまいません。次から次へと読み進んで、トットちゃんといっしょに学校生活を楽しんでください。

講談社インターナショナル

Publisher's Preface to This Edition

Tetsuko Kuroyanagi's *Totto-chan: The Little Girl at the Window*, first published by Kodansha in 1981, is a record-breaking best-seller whose continuing appeal to everyone from children to the elderly, irrespective of both age and gender, has already sold 7 million copies.

Hoping to kindle its fascination anew, we have selected 30 chapters from the original 61 to present them in this Bilingual Books edition.

Now, when family values and relations between children, the family and society are being closely questioned, we feel it is time to remind readers of that happy little world filled with the sound of artless, innocent laughter, and the courage and love that reaches beyond differences of race and nationality.

Furthermore, this bilingual format will give readers the fun of enjoying the book in either Japanese or English and comparing the two. Vivid and lively, and teeming with easy, everyday conversational phrases, *Totto-chan: The Little Girl at the Window* can even serve as a language text.

We have included plenty of Chihiro Iwasaki's delightful illustrations. Matching the stories so perfectfully, they bring *Totto-chan* to life more vividly than ever. Whether you read the book in English or Japanese, you are sure to enjoy Totto-chan's succession of hilarious and heartwarming adventures at her most unusual school.

KODANSHA INTERNATIONAL

目　次

Contents

はじめての駅

自由が丘の駅で、大井町線から降りると、ママは、トットちゃんの手をひっぱって、改札口を出ようとした。トットちゃんは、それまで、あまり電車に乗ったことがなかったから、大切に握っていた切符をあげちゃうのは、もったいないなと思った。そこで、改札口のおじさんに、

「この切符、もらっちゃいけない?」

と聞いた。おじさんは、

「ダメだよ」

というと、トットちゃんの手から、切符を取りあげた。トットちゃんは、改札口の箱にいっぱい溜っている切符をさして聞いた。

「これ、全部、おじさんの?」

おじさんは、他の出て行く人の切符をひったくりながら答えた。

「おじさんのじゃないよ、駅のだから」

「へーえ……」

トットちゃんは、未練がましく、箱をのぞきこみながらいった。

「私、大人になったら、切符を売る人になろうと思うわ」

おじさんは、はじめて、トットちゃんをチラリと見て、いった。

「うちの男の子も、駅で働きたいって、いってるから、一緒にやるといいよ」

トットちゃんは、少し離れて、おじさんを見た。おじさんは肥

The Railroad Station

They got off the Oimachi train at Jiyugaoka Station, and Mother took Totto-chan by the hand to lead her through the ticket gate. She had hardly ever been on a train before and was reluctant to give up the precious ticket she was clutching.

"May I keep it?" Totto-chan asked the ticket collector.

"No, you can't," he replied, taking it from her.

She pointed to his box filled with tickets. "Are those all yours?"

"No, they belong to the railroad station," he replied, as he snatched away tickets from people going out.

"Oh." Totto-chan gazed longingly into the box and went on, "When I grow up I'm going to sell railroad tickets!"

The ticket collector glanced at her for the first time. "My little boy wants a job in the station, too, so you can work together."

Totto-chan stepped to one side and took a good look at the ticket collector. He was plump and wore glasses and seemed rather kind.

っていて、眼鏡をかけていて、よく見ると、やさしそうなところもあった。
「ふん……」
　トットちゃんは、手を腰にあてて、観察しながらいった。
「おじさんとこの子と、一緒にやってもいいけど、考えとくわ。あたし、これから新しい学校に行くんで、忙しいから」
　そういうと、トットちゃんは、待ってるママのところに走っていった。そして、こう叫んだ。
「私、切符屋さんになろうと思うんだ！」
　ママは、おどろきもしないで、いった。
「でも、スパイになるっていってたのは、どうするの?」
　トットちゃんは、ママに手をとられて歩き出しながら、考えた。
（そうだわ。昨日までは、絶対にスパイになろう、って決めてたのに。でも、いまの切符をいっぱい箱にしまっておく人になるのも、とても、いいと思うわ）
「そうだ!!」
　トットちゃんは、いいことを思いついて、ママの顔をのぞきながら、大声をはりあげていった。
「ねえ、本当はスパイなんだけど、切符屋さんなのは、どう?」
　ママは答えなかった。本当のことをいうと、ママはとても不安だったのだ。もし、これから行く小学校で、トットちゃんのことを、あずかってくれなかったら……。小さい花のついた、フェルトの帽子をかぶっている、ママの、きれいな顔が、少しまじめになった。そして、道をとびはねながら、なにかを早口でしゃべってるトットちゃんを見た。トットちゃんは、ママの心配を知らなかったから、顔があうと、うれしそうに笑っていった。
「ねえ、私、やっぱり、どっちもやめて、チンドン屋さんになる!!」
　ママは、多少、絶望的な気分でいった。
「さあ、遅れるわ。校長先生が待ってらっしゃるんだから。も

"Hmm." She put her hands on her hips and carefully considered the idea. "I wouldn't mind at all working with your son," she said. "I'll think it over. But I'm rather busy just now as I'm on my way to a new school."

She ran to where Mother waited, shouting, "I'm going to be a ticket seller!"

Mother wasn't surprised, but she said, "I thought you were going to be a spy."

As Totto-chan began walking along holding Mother's hand, she remembered that until the day before she had been quite sure she wanted to be a spy. But what fun it would be to be in charge of a box full of tickets!

"That's it!" A splendid idea occurred to her. She looked up at Mother and informed her of it at the top of her voice, "Couldn't I be a ticket seller who's really a spy?"

Mother didn't reply. Under her felt hat with its little flowers, her lovely face was serious. The fact was Mother was very worried. What if they wouldn't have Totto-chan at the new school? She looked at Totto-chan skipping along the road chattering to herself. Totto-chan didn't know Mother was worried, so when their eyes met, she said gaily, "I've changed my mind. I think I'll join one of those little bands of street musicians who go about advertising new stores!"

There was a touch of despair in Mother's voice as she said, "Come on, we'll be late. We mustn't keep the headmaster waiting. No more chatter. Look where

う、おしゃべりしないで、前を向いて、歩いてちょうだい」
　二人の目の前に、小さい学校の門が見えてきた。

窓ぎわのトットちゃん

　新しい学校の門をくぐる前に、トットちゃんのママが、なぜ不安なのかを説明すると、それはトットちゃんが、小学校一年なのにかかわらず、すでに学校を退学になったからだった。一年生で!!
　つい先週のことだった。ママはトットちゃんの担任の先生に呼ばれて、はっきり、こういわれた。
「おたくのお嬢さんがいると、クラス中の迷惑になります。よその学校にお連れください！」
　若くて美しい女の先生は、ため息をつきながら、くり返した。
「本当に困ってるんです！」
　ママはびっくりした。（一体、どんなことを……。クラス中の迷惑になる、どんなことを、あの子がするんだろうか……）
　先生は、カールしたまつ毛をパチパチさせ、パーマのかかった短い内巻の毛を手でなでながら説明にとりかかった。
「まず、授業中に、机のフタを、百ぺんくらい、開けたり閉めたりするんです。そこで私が、『用事がないのに、開けたり閉めたりしてはいけません』と申しますと、おたくのお嬢さんは、ノートから、筆箱、教科書、全部を机の中にしまってしまって、ひとつひとつ取り出すんです。例えば、書き取りをするとしますね。するとお嬢さんは、まずフタを開けて、ノートを取り出した、と思うが早いか、パタン！　とフタを閉めてしまいます。そして、すぐにまた開けて頭を中につっこんで筆箱から〝ア〟を書くための

you're going and walk properly."

Ahead of them, in the distance, the gate of a small school was gradually coming into view.

The Little Girl at the Window

The reason Mother was worried was because although Totto-chan had only just started school, she had already been expelled. Fancy being expelled from the first grade!

It had happened only a week ago. Mother had been sent for by Totto-chan's homeroom teacher, who came straight to the point. "Your daughter disrupts my whole class. I must ask you to take her to another school." The pretty young teacher sighed. "I'm really at the end of my tether."

Mother was completely taken aback. What on earth did Totto-chan do to disrupt the whole class, she wondered?

Blinking nervously and touching her hair, cut in a short pageboy style, the teacher started to explain. "Well, to begin with, she opens and shuts her desk hundreds of times. I've said that no one is to open or shut their desk unless they have to take something out or put something away. So your daughter is constantly taking something out and putting something away—taking out or putting away her notebook, her pencil box, her textbooks, and everything else in her desk. For

鉛筆を出すと、いそいで閉めて、〝ア〟を書きます。ところが、うまく書けなかったり、間違えたりしますね。そうすると、フタを開けて、また頭をつっこんで、ケシゴムを出し、閉めると、いそいでケシゴムを使い、次に、すごい早さで開けて、ケシゴムをしまって、フタを閉めてしまいます。で、すぐ、また開けるので見てますと、〝ア〟ひとつだけ書いて、道具をひとつひとつ、全部しまうんです。鉛筆をしまい、閉めて、また開けてノートをしまい……という風に。そして、次の〝イ〟のときに、また、ノートから始まって、鉛筆、ケシゴム……そのたびに、私の目の前で、目まぐるしく、机のフタが開いたり閉まったり。私、目がまわるんです。でも、一応、用事があるんですから、『いけない』とは申せませんけど……」

先生のまつ毛が、そのときを思い出したように、パチパチと早くなった。

そこまで聞いて、ママには、トットちゃんが、なんで、学校の机を、そんなに開けたり閉めたりするのか、ちょっとわかった。というのは、初めて学校に行って帰ってきた日に、トットちゃん

instance, say we are going to write the alphabet, your daughter opens her desk, takes out her notebook, and bangs the top down. Then she opens her desk again, puts her head inside, gets out a pencil, quickly shuts the desk, and writes an 'A.' If she's written it badly or made a mistake she opens the desk again, gets out an eraser, shuts the desk, erases the letter, then opens and shuts the desk again to put away the eraser—all at top speed. When she's written the 'A' over again, she puts every single item back into the desk, one by one. She puts away the pencil, shuts the desk, then opens it again to put away the notebook. Then, when she gets to the next letter, she goes through it all again—first the notebook, then the pencil, then the eraser—opening and shutting her desk every single time. It makes my head spin. And I can't scold her because she opens and shuts it each time for a reason."

The teacher's long eyelashes fluttered even more as if she were reliving the scene in her mind.

It suddenly dawned on Mother why Totto-chan opened and shut her desk so often. She remembered how excited Totto-chan had been when she came home from her first day at school. She had said, "School's wonderful! My

が、ひどく興奮して、こうママに報告したことを思い出したからだった。

『ねえ、学校って、すごいの。家の机の引き出しは、こんな風に、ひっぱるのだけど、学校のはフタが上にあがるの。ごみ箱のフタと同じなんだけど、もっとツルツルで、いろんなものが、しまえて、とってもいいんだ！』

ママには、今まで見たことのない机の前で、トットちゃんが面白がって、開けたり閉めたりしてる様子が目に見えるようだった。そして、それは、（そんなに悪いことではないし、第一、だんだん馴れてくれば、そんなに開けたり閉めたりしなくなるだろう）と考えたけど、先生には、

「よく注意しますから」

といった。

ところが、先生は、それまでの調子より声をもう少し高くして、こういった。

「それだけなら、よろしいんですけど！」

ママは、少し身がちぢむような気がした。先生は、体を少し前にのり出すといった。

「机で音を立ててないな、と思うと、今度は、授業中、立ってるんです。ずーっと！」

ママは、またびっくりしたので聞いた。

「立ってるって、どこにでございましょうか？」

先生は少し怒った風にいった。

「教室の窓のところです！」

ママは、わけがわからないので、続けて質問した。

「窓のところで、なにをしてるんでしょうか？」

先生は、半分、叫ぶような声でいった。

「チンドン屋を呼びこむためです!!」

desk at home has drawers you pull out, but the one at school has a top you lift up. It's like a box, and you can keep all sorts of things inside. It's super!"

Mother pictured her delightedly opening and shutting the lid of this new desk. And Mother didn't think it was all that naughty either. Anyway, Totto-chan would probably stop doing it as soon as the novelty wore off. But all she said to the teacher was, "I'll speak to her about it."

The teacher's voice rose in pitch as she continued, "I wouldn't mind if that was all."

Mother flinched as the teacher leaned forward. "When she's not making a clatter with her desk, she's standing up. All through class!"

"Standing up? Where?" asked Mother, surprised.

"At the window," the teacher replied crossly.

"Why does she stand at the window?" Mother asked, puzzled.

"So she can invite the street musicians over!" she almost shrieked.

先生の話を、まとめて見ると、こういうことになるらしかった。
一時間目に、机のパタパタを、かなりやると、それ以後は、机を離れて、窓のところに立って外を見ている。そこで、静かにしていてくれるのなら、立っててもいい、と先生が思った矢先に突然、トットちゃんは、大きい声で、「チンドン屋さーん」と外にむかって叫んだ。だいたい、この教室の窓というのが、トットちゃんにとっては幸福なことに、先生にとっては不幸なことに、一階にあり、しかも通りは目の前だった。そして境といえば、低い、いけ垣があるだけだったから、トットちゃんは、簡単に、通りを歩いてる人と、話が出来るわけだったのだ。さて、通りかかったチンドン屋さんは、呼ばれたから教室の下まで来る。するとトットちゃんは、うれしそうに、クラス中のみんなに呼びかけた。「来たわよ——」勉強してたクラス中の子供は、全員、その声で窓のところに、つめかけて、口々に叫ぶ。「チンドン屋さーん」すると、トットちゃんは、チンドン屋さんに頼む。
「ねえ、ちょっとだけ、やってみて?」
学校のそばを通るときは、音をおさえめにしているチンドン屋さんも、せっかくの頼みだからというので盛大に始める。クラリネットや鉦やタイコや、三味線で。その間、先生がどうしてるか、といえば、一段落つくまで、ひとり教壇で、じーっと待ってるしかない。(この一曲が終わるまでの辛抱なんだから)と自分にいいきかせながら。
さて、一曲終わると、チンドン屋さんは去って行き、生徒たちは、それぞれの席にもどる。ところが、驚いたことに、トットちゃんは、窓のところから動かない。「どうして、まだ、そこにいるのですか?」という先生の問いに、トットちゃんは、大まじめに答えた。
「だって、また違うチンドン屋さんが来たら、お話しなきゃならないし。それから、さっきのチンドン屋さんが、また、もどってきたら、大変だからです」

The gist of the teacher's story was that after an hour of almost constantly banging her desk top, Totto-chan would leave her desk and stand by the window, looking out. Then, just as the teacher was beginning to think that as long as she was quiet she might just as well stay there, Totto-chan would suddenly call out to a passing band of garishly dressed street musicians. To Totto-chan's delight and the teacher's tribulation, the classroom was on the ground floor looking out on the street. There was only a low hedge in between, so anyone in the classroom could easily talk to people going by. When Totto-chan called to them, the street musicians would come right over to the window. Whereupon, said the teacher, Totto-chan would announce the fact to the whole room, "Here they are!" and all the children would crowd by the window and call out to the musicians.

"Play something," Totto-chan would say, and the little band, which usually passed the school quietly, would put on a rousing performance for the pupils with their clarinet, gongs, drums, and shamisen. While as for the teacher, there was nothing she could do but wait there calmly by herself on the dais until there was a pause, telling herself she just had to be patient until the piece ended.

Finally, when the music finished, the musicians would leave and the students would go back to their seats. All except Totto-chan. When the teacher asked, "Why are you still at the window?" Totto-chan replied, quite seriously, "Another band might come by. And,

「これじゃ、授業にならない、ということが、おわかりでしょう?」
　話してるうちに、先生は、かなり感情的になってきて、ママにいった。ママは、(なるほど、これでは先生も、お困りだわ)と思いかけた。とたん、先生は、また一段と大きな声で、こういった。
「それに……」
　ママはびっくりしながらも、なさけない思いで先生に聞いた。
「まだ、あるんでございましょうか……」
　先生は、すぐ言った。
「〝まだ〟というように、数えられるくらいなら、こうやって、やめていただきたい、とお願いはいたしません!!」
　それから先生は、少し息をしずめて、ママの顔を見ていった。
「昨日のことですが、例によって、窓のところに立っているので、またチンドン屋だと思って授業をしておりましたら、これが、また大きな声で、いきなり、『なにしてるの?』と、誰かに、なにかを聞いているんですね。相手は、私のほうから見えませんので、誰だろう、と思っておりますと、また大きな声で、『ねえ、なにしてるの?』って。それも、今度は、通りにでなく、上のほうにむかって聞いてるんです。私も気になりまして、相手の返事が聞こえるかしら、と耳をすましてみましたが、返事がないんです。お嬢さんは、それでも、さかんに、『ねえ、なにしてるの?』を続けるので、授業にもさしさわりがあるので、窓のところに行って、お嬢さんの話しかけてる相手が誰なのか、見てみようと思いました。窓から顔を出して上を見ましたら、なんと、つばめが、教室の屋根の下に、巣を作って

anyway, it would be such a shame if the others came back and we missed them."

"You can see how disruptive all this is, can't you?" said the teacher emotionally. Mother was beginning to sympathize with her when she began again in an even shriller voice, "And then, besides . . ."

"What else does she do?" asked Mother, with a sinking feeling.

"What else?" exclaimed the teacher. "If I could even count the things she does I wouldn't be asking you to take her away."

The teacher composed herself a little, and looked straight at Mother. "Yesterday, Totto-chan was standing at the window as usual, and I went on with the lesson thinking she was just waiting for the street musicians, when she suddenly called out to somebody, 'What are you doing?' From where I was I couldn't see who she was talking to, and I wondered what was going on. Then she called out again, 'What are you doing?' She wasn't addressing anyone in the road but somebody high up somewhere. I couldn't help being curious, and tried to hear the reply, but there wasn't any. In spite of that, your daughter kept on calling out, 'What are you doing?' so often I couldn't teach, so I went over to the window to see who your daughter was talking to. When I put my head out of the window and looked up, I saw it was a pair of swallows making a nest under the classroom eaves. She was talking to the swallows! Now, I

いるんです。その、つばめに聞いてるんですね。そりゃ私も、子供の気持ちが、わからないわけじゃありませんから、つばめに聞いてることを、馬鹿げている、とは申しません。でも、授業中に、あんな声で、つばめに、『なにをしてるのか?』と聞かなくてもいいと、私は思うんです」

そして先生は、ママが、一体なんとおわびをしよう、と口を開きかけたのより、早くいった。

「それから、こういうことも、ございました。初めての図画の時間のことですが、国旗を描いてごらんなさい、と私が申しましたら、他の子は、画用紙に、ちゃんと日の丸を描いたんですが、おたくのお嬢さんは、朝日新聞の模様のような、軍艦旗を描き始めました。それなら、それでいい、と思ってましたら、突然、旗のまわりに、ふさを、つけ始めたんです。ふさ。よく青年団とか、そういった旗についてます、あの、ふさです。で、それも、まあ、どこかで見たのだろうから、と思っておりました。ところが、ちょっと目を離したスキに、まあ、黄色のふさを、机にまで、どんどん描いちゃってるんです。だいたい画用紙に、ほぼ一杯に旗を描いたんですから、ふさの余裕は、もともと、あまり無かったんですが、それに、黄色のクレヨンで、ゴシゴシふさを描いたんですね。それが、はみ出しちゃって、画用紙をどかしたら、机に、ひどい黄色のギザギザが残ってしまって、ふいても、こすっても、とれません。まあ、幸いなことは、ギザギザが三方向だけだった、ってことでしょうか?」

ママは、ちぢこまりながらも、いそいで質問した。

「三方向っていうのは……」

先生は、そろそろ疲れてきた、という様子だったが、それでも親切にいった。

「旗竿を左はじに描きましたから、旗のギザギザは、三方だけだったんでございます」

ママは、少し助かった、と思って、

understand children, and so I'm not saying that talking to swallows is nonsense. It is just that I feel it is quite unnecessary to ask swallows what they are doing in the middle of class."

Before Mother could open her mouth to apologize, the teacher went on, "Then there was the drawing class episode. I asked the children to draw the Japanese flag, and all the others drew it correctly but your daughter started drawing the navy flag—you know, the one with the rays. Nothing wrong with that, I thought. But then she suddenly started to draw a fringe all around it. A fringe! You know, like those fringes on youth group banners. She's probably seen one somewhere. But before I realized what she was doing, she had drawn a yellow fringe that went right off the edge of the paper and onto her desk. You see, her flag took up most of the paper, so there wasn't enough room for the fringe. She took her yellow crayon and all around her flag she made hundreds of strokes that extended beyond the paper, so that when she lifted up the paper her desk was a mass of dreadful yellow marks that wouldn't come off no matter how hard we rubbed. Fortunately, the lines were only on three sides."

Puzzled, Mother asked quickly, "What do you mean, only three sides?"

Although she seemed to be getting tired, the teacher was kind enough to explain. "She drew a flagpole on the left, so the fringe was only on three sides of the flag."

「はあ、それで三方だけ……」

といった。すると、先生は、次に、とっても、ゆっくりの口調で、ひとことずつ区切って、いった。

「ただし、そのかわり、旗竿のはじが、やはり、机に、はみ出して、残っております!!」

それから先生は立ちあがると、かなり冷たい感じで、とどめをさすようにいった。

「それと、迷惑しているのは、私だけではございません。隣(とな)りの一年生の受持ちの先生もお困りのことが、あるそうですから……」

ママは、決心しないわけには、いかなかった。(たしかに、これじゃ、他の生徒さんに、ご迷惑すぎる。どこか、他の学校を探して、移したほうが、よさそうだ。なんとか、あの子の性格がわかっていただけて、みんなと一緒にやっていくことを教えてくださるような学校に……)

そうして、ママが、あっちこっち、かけずりまわって見つけたのが、これから行こうとしている学校、というわけだったのだ。

ママは、この退学のことを、トットちゃんに話していなかった。話しても、なにがいけなかったのか、わからないだろうし、また、そんなことで、トットちゃんが、コンプレックスを持つのも、よくないと思ったから、(いつか、大きくなったら、話しましょう)と、きめていた。ただ、トットちゃんには、こういった。

「新しい学校に行ってみない?　いい学校だって話よ」

トットちゃんは、少し考えてから、いった。

「行くけど……」

ママは、(この子は、いま何を考えてるのだろうか)と思った。(うすうす、退学のこと、気がついていたんだろうか……)

次の瞬間(しゅんかん)、トットちゃんは、ママの腕(うで)の中に、とびこんで来て、いった。

「ねえ、今度の学校に、いいチンドン屋さん、来るかな?」

Mother felt somewhat relieved. "I see, only on three sides."

Whereupon the teacher said very slowly, emphasizing each word, "But most of the flagpole went off the paper, too, and is still on the desk as well."

Then the teacher got up and said coldly, as a sort of parting shot, "I'm not the only one who is upset. The teacher in the classroom next door has also had trouble."

Mother obviously had to do something about it. It wasn't fair to the other pupils. She'd have to find another school, a school where they would understand her little girl and teach her how to get along with other people.

The school they were on their way to was one Mother had found after a good deal of searching.

Mother did not tell Totto-chan she had been expelled. She realized Totto-chan wouldn't understand what she had done wrong and she didn't want her to get any complexes, so she decided not to tell Totto-chan until she was grown-up. All Mother had said was, "How would you like to go to a new school? I've heard of a very nice one."

"All right," Totto-chan had replied, after thinking it over. "But . . ."

"What is it now?" thought Mother. "Does she realize she's been expelled?"

But a moment later Totto-chan was asking joyfully, "Do you think the street musicians will come to the next school?"

とにかく、そんなわけで、トットちゃんとママは、新しい学校にむかって、歩いているのだった。

新しい学校

学校の門が、はっきり見えるところまで来て、トットちゃんは、立ち止まった。なぜなら、この間まで行っていた学校の門は、立派なコンクリートみたいな柱で、学校の名前も、大きく書いてあった。ところが、この新しい学校の門ときたら、低い木で、しかも葉っぱが生えていた。

「地面から生えてる門ね」

と、トットちゃんはママにいった。そうして、こう、つけ加えた。

「きっと、どんどん生えて、今に電信柱より高くなるわ」

たしかに、その二本の門は、根っこのある木だった。トットちゃんは、門に近づくと、いきなり顔を、ななめにした。なぜかといえば、門にぶらさげてある学校の名前を書いた札（ふだ）が、風に吹（ふ）かれたのか、ななめになっていたからだった。

「トモエがくえん」

トットちゃんは、顔をななめにしたまま、表札（ひょうさつ）を読みあげた。

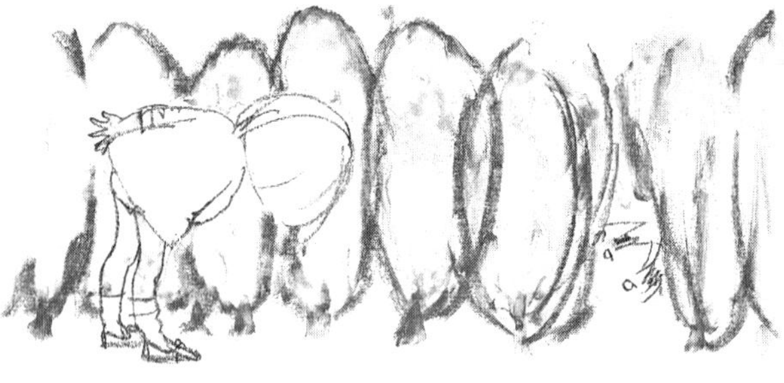

And that is why Totto-chan and her mother were walking along now towards the new school.

The New School

When she saw the gate of the new school, Totto-chan stopped. The gate of the school she used to go to had fine concrete pillars with the name of the school in large characters. But the gate of this new school simply consisted of two rather short posts that still had twigs and leaves on them.

"This gate's growing," said Totto-chan. "It'll probably go on growing till it's taller than the telephone poles!"

The two "gateposts" were clearly trees with roots. When she got closer, she suddenly put her head to one side she had to do that because the wind had blown the sign askew. With her head still cocked to one side, Totto-chan read out the name on the sign.

"To-mo-e Ga-ku-en."

そして、ママに、
「トモエって、なあに?」
　と聞こうとしたときだった。トットちゃんの目の端に、夢としか思えないものが見えたのだった。トットちゃんは、身をかがめると、門の植えこみの、すき間に頭をつっこんで、門の中をのぞいてみた。どうしよう、見えたんだけど！
「ママ！　あれ、本当の電車?　校庭に並んでるの」
　それは、走っていない、本当の電車が六台、教室用に、置かれてあるのだった。トットちゃんは、夢のように思った。〝電車の教室……。〟
　電車の窓が、朝の光をうけて、キラキラと光っていた。目を輝かして、のぞいているトットちゃんの、ホッペタも、光っていた。

気にいったわ

　次の瞬間、トットちゃんは、「わーい」と歓声をあげると、電車の教室のほうにむかって走り出した。そして、走りながら、ママにむかって叫んだ。
「ねえ、早く、動かない電車に乗ってみよう！」
　ママは、おどろいて走り出した。もとバスケットボールの選手だったママの足は、トットちゃんより速かったから、トットちゃんが、あと、ちょっとでドア、というときに、スカートをつかまえられてしまった。ママは、スカートのはしを、ぎっちり握ったまま、トットちゃんにいった。
「だめよ。この電車は、この学校のお教室なんだし、あなたは、まだ、この学校に入れていただいてないんだから。もし、どうしても、この電車に乗りたいんだったら、これからお目にかかる校

Then just as Totto-chan was about to ask Mother what "Tomoe" meant, she caught a glimpse of something that made her think she must be dreaming. She squatted down and peered through the shrubbery to get a better look, and she couldn't believe her eyes.

"Mother, is that really a train? There, in the school grounds!"

For its classrooms, the school had made use of six abandoned railroad cars. To Totto-chan it seemed something you might dream about. A school in a train!

The windows of the railroad cars sparkled in the morning sunlight. But the eyes of the rosy-cheeked little girl gazing at them through the shrubbery sparkled even more.

"I Like This School!"

A moment later, Totto-chan let out a whoop of joy and started running toward the "train school," calling out to Mother over her shoulder, "Come on, hurry, let's get on this train that's standing still."

Startled, Mother began to run after her. Mother had been on a basketball team once, so she was faster than Totto-chan and caught hold of her dress just as she reached a door.

"You can't go in yet," said Mother, holding her back. "The cars are classrooms, and you haven't even been accepted here yet. If you really want to get on this train, you'll have to be nice and polite to the headmas-

長先生とちゃんと、お話ししてちょうだい。そして、うまくいったら、この学校に通えるんだから。わかった?」
　トットちゃんは、(いま乗れないのは、とても残念なことだ)と思ったけど、ママのいう通りにしようと決めたから、大きな声で、
「うん」
　といって、それから、いそいで、つけたした。
「私、この学校、とっても気に入ったわ」
　ママは、トットちゃんが気に入ったかどうかより、校長先生が、トットちゃんを気に入ってくださるかどうかが問題なのよ、といいたい気がしたけど、とにかく、トットちゃんのスカートから手を離し、手をつないで校長室のほうに歩き出した。
　どの電車も静かで、ちょっと前に、一時間目の授業が始まったようだった。あまり広くない校庭のまわりには、塀のかわりに、いろんな種類の木が植わっていて、花壇には、赤や黄色の花がいっぱい咲いていた。
　校長室は、電車ではなく、ちょうど、門から正面に見える扇型に広がった七段くらいある石の階段を上がった、その右手にあった。
　トットちゃんは、ママの手をふりきると、階段をかけ上がって行ったが、急に止まって、振りむいた。だから、うしろから行ったママは、もう少しで、トットちゃんと正面衝突するところだった。
「どうしたの?」
　ママは、トットちゃんの気がかわったのかと思って、いそいで聞いた。トットちゃんは、ちょうど階段の一番うえに立った形だったけど、まじめな顔をして、小声でママに聞いた。
「ねえ、これから逢いに行く人って、駅の人なんじゃないの?」
　ママは、かなり辛抱づよい人間だったから……というか、面白がりやだったから、やはり小声になって、トットちゃんに顔をつ

ter. We're going to call on him now, and if all goes well, you'll be able to go to this school. Do you understand?"

Totto-chan was awfully disappointed not to get on the "train" right away, but she decided she had better do as Mother told her.

"All right," she said. And then added, "I like this school a lot."

Mother felt like telling her it wasn't a matter of whether she liked the school but of whether the headmaster liked her. But she just let go of Totto-chan's dress, took hold of her hand, and started walking toward the headmaster's office.

All the railroad cars were quiet, for the first classes of the day had begun. Instead of a wall, the not very spacious school grounds were surrounded by trees, and there were flower beds full of red and yellow flowers.

The headmaster's office wasn't in a railroad car, but was on the right-hand side of a one-story building that stood at the top of a semicircular flight of about seven stone steps opposite the gate.

Totto-chan let go of Mother's hand and raced up the steps, then turned around abruptly, almost causing Mother to run into her.

"What's the matter?" Mother asked, fearing Totto-chan might have changed her mind about the school.

Standing above her on the top step, Totto-chan whispered to Mother in all seriousness, "The man we're going to see must be a stationmaster!"

Mother had plenty of patience as well as a great

けて、聞いた。
「どうして?」
　トットちゃんは、ますます声をひそめていった。
「だってさ、校長先生って、ママいったけど、こんなに電車、いっぱい持ってるんだから、本当は、駅の人なんじゃないの?」
　たしかに、電車の払い下げを校舎にしている学校なんて珍しいから、トットちゃんの疑問も、もっとものこと、とママも思ったけど、この際、説明してるヒマはないので、こういった。
「じゃ、あなた、校長先生に伺ってごらんなさい、自分で。それと、あなたのパパのことを考えてみて?　パパはヴァイオリンを弾く人で、いくつかヴァイオリンを持ってるけど、ヴァイオリン屋さんじゃないでしょう?　そういう人もいるのよ」
　トットちゃんは、「そうか」というと、ママと手をつないだ。

校長先生

　トットちゃんとママが入っていくと、部屋の中にいた男の人が椅子から立ちあがった。
　その人は、頭の毛が薄くなっていて、前のほうの歯が抜けていて、顔の血色がよく、背はあまり高くないけど、肩や腕が、がっちりしていて、ヨレヨレの黒の三つ揃いを、キチンと着ていた。
　トットちゃんは、いそいで、おじぎをしてから、元気よく聞いた。
「校長先生か、駅の人か、どっち?」
　ママが、あわてて説明しよう、とする前に、その人は、笑いながら答えた。
「校長先生だよ」
　トットちゃんは、とってもうれしそうにいった。
「よかった。じゃ、おねがい。私、この学校に入りたいの」

sense of fun. She put her face close to Totto-chan's and whispered, "Why?"

Totto-chan whispered back, "You said he was the headmaster, but if he owns all these trains, he must be a stationmaster."

Mother had to admit it was unusual for a school to make use of old railroad cars, but there was no time to explain. She simply said, "Why don't you ask him yourself? And, anyway, what about Daddy? He plays the violin and owns several violins, but that doesn't make our house a violin shop, does it?"

"No, it doesn't," Totto-chan agreed, catching hold of Mother's hand.

The Headmaster

When Mother and Totto-chan went in, the man in the office got up from his chair.

His hair was thin on top and he had a few teeth missing, but his face was a healthy color. Although he wasn't very tall, he had solid shoulders and arms and was neatly dressed in a rather shabby black three-piece suit.

With a hasty bow, Totto-chan asked him spiritedly, "What are you, a schoolmaster or a stationmaster?"

Mother was embarrassed, but before she had time to explain, he laughed and replied, "I'm the headmaster of this school."

Totto-chan was delighted. "Oh, I'm so glad," she

　校長先生は、椅子をトットちゃんにすすめると、ママのほうを向いていった。
「じゃ、僕は、これからトットちゃんと話がありますから、もう、お帰りくださって結構です」
　ほんのちょっとの間、トットちゃんは、少し心細い気がしたけど、なんとなく、（この校長先生とならいいや）と思った。ママは、いさぎよく先生にいった。
「じゃ、よろしく、お願いします」
　そして、ドアを閉めて出ていった。
　校長先生は、トットちゃんの前に椅子をひっぱって来て、とても近い位置に、むかい合わせに腰をかけると、こういった。
「さあ、なんでも、先生に話してごらん。話したいこと、全部」
「話したいこと!?」
（なにか聞かれて、お返事するのかな？）　と思っていたトットちゃんは、「なんでも話していい」と聞いて、ものすごくうれしくなって、すぐ話し始めた。順序も、話しかたも、少しグチャグチャだったけど、一生懸命に話した。
　いま乗って来た電車が速かったこと。
　駅の改札口のおじさんに、お願いしたけど、切符をくれなかったこと。
　前に行ってた学校の受持ちの女の先生は、顔がきれいだということ。
　その学校には、つばめの巣があること。
　家には、ロッキーという茶色の犬がいて〝お手〟と〝ごめんくださいませ〟と、ごはんのあとで、〝満足、満足〟が出来ること。
　幼稚園のとき、ハサミを口の中に入れて、チョキチョキやると、「舌を切ります」と先生が怒ったけど、何回もやっちゃったっていうこと。
　洟が出てきたときは、いつまでも、ズルズルやってると、ママ

said, "because I want to ask you a favor. I'd like to come to your school."

The headmaster offered her a chair and turned to Mother. "You may go home now. I want to talk to Totto-chan."

Totto-chan had a moment's uneasiness, but somehow felt she would get along all right with this man.

"Well, then, I'll leave her with you," Mother said bravely, and shut the door behind her as she went out.

The headmaster drew over a chair and put it facing Totto-chan, and when they were both sitting down close together, he said, "Now then, tell me all about yourself. Tell me anything at all you want to talk about."

"Anything I like?" Totto-chan had expected him to ask questions she would have to answer. When he said she could talk about anything she wanted, she was so happy she began straight away. It was all a bit higgledy-piggledy, but she talked for all she was worth. She told the headmaster how fast the train went that they had come on; how she had asked the ticket collector but he wouldn't let her keep her ticket; how pretty her homeroom teacher was at the other school; about the swallows' nest; about their brown dog, Rocky, who could do all sorts of tricks; how she used to go snip-snip with the scissors inside her mouth at kindergarten and the teacher said she mustn't do that because she might cut her tongue off, but she did it anyway; how she always blew her nose because Mother scolded her if it was

に叱られるから、なるべく早くかむこと。
パパは、海で泳ぐのが上手で、飛び込みだって出来ること。
こういったことを、次から次と、トットちゃんは話した。先生は、笑ったり、うなずいたり、「それから?」とかいったりしてくださったから、うれしくて、トットちゃんは、いつまでも話した。でも、とうとう、話が無くなった。トットちゃんが、口をつぐんで考えていると、先生はいった。
「もう、ないかい?」
トットちゃんは、これでおしまいにしてしまうのは、残念だと思った。
せっかく、話を、いっぱい聞いてもらう、いいチャンスなのに。
(なにか、話は、ないかなあ……)
頭の中が、いそがしく動いた。と思ったら、「よかった!」話が見つかった。
それは、その日、トットちゃんが着てる洋服のことだった。たいがいの洋服は、ママが手製で作ってくれるのだけれど、今日のは、買ったものだった。というのも、なにしろトットちゃんが夕方、外から帰って来たとき、どの洋服もビリビリで、ときには、ジャキジャキのときもあったし、どうしてそうなるのか、ママにも絶対わからないのだけれど、白い木綿でゴム入りのパンツまで、ビリビリになっているのだから。トットちゃんの話によると、よその家の庭をつっきって垣根をもぐったり、原っぱの鉄条網の間をくぐるとき、「こんなになっちゃうんだ」ということなのだけれど、とにかく、そんな具合で、結局、今朝、家を出るとき、ママの手製の、しゃれたのは、どれもビリビリで、仕方なく、前に買ったのを着てきたのだった。それはワンピースで、エンジとグレーの細かいチェックで、布地はジャージーだから、悪くはないけど、衿にしてある、花の刺繍の、赤い色が、ママは、「趣味が悪い」といっていた。そのことを、トットちゃんは、思い出したの

runny; what a good swimmer Daddy was, and how he could dive as well. She went on and on. The headmaster would laugh, nod, and say, “And then?” And Totto-chan was so happy she kept right on talking. But finally she ran out of things to say. She sat with her mouth closed trying hard to think of something.

“Haven’t you anything more you can tell me?” asked the headmaster.

What a shame to stop now, Totto-chan thought. It was such a wonderful chance. Wasn’t there anything else she could talk about, she wondered, racking her brains? Then she had an idea.

She could tell him about the dress she was wearing that day. Mother made most of her dresses, but this one came from a shop. Her clothes were always torn when she came home in the late afternoon. Some of the rips were quite bad. Mother never knew how they got that way. Even her white cotton panties were sometimes in shreds. She explained to the headmaster that they got torn when she crossed other people’s gardens by crawling under their fences, and when she burrowed under the barbed wire around vacant lots. So this morning, she said, when she was getting dressed to come here, all the nice dresses Mother had made

だった。だから、いそいで椅子から降りると、衿を手で持ち上げて、先生のそばに行き、こういった。
「この衿ね、ママ、嫌いなんだって！」
それをいってしまったら、どう考えてみても、本当に、話は、もう無くなった。トットちゃんは、（少し悲しい）と思った。トットちゃんが、そう思ったとき、先生が立ち上がった。そして、トットちゃんの頭に、大きくて暖かい手を置くと、
「じゃ、これで、君は、この学校の生徒だよ」
そういった。……そのとき、トットちゃんは、なんだか、生まれて初めて、本当に好きな人に逢ったような気がした。だって、生まれてから今日まで、こんな長い時間、自分の話を聞いてくれた人は、いなかったんだもの。そして、その長い時間のあいだ、一度だって、あくびをしたり、退屈そうにしないで、トットちゃんが話してるのと同じように、身をのり出して、一生懸命、聞いてくれたんだもの。
トットちゃんは、このとき、まだ時計が読めなかったんだけど、それでも長い時間、と思ったくらいなんだから、もし読めたら、ビックリしたに違いない。そして、もっと先生に感謝したに違いない。というのは、トットちゃんとママが学校に着いたのが八時で、校長室で全部の話が終わって、トットちゃんが、この学校の生徒になった、と決まったとき、先生が懐中時計を見て、「ああ、お弁当の時間だな」といったから、つまり、たっぷり四時間、先生は、トットちゃんの話を聞いてくれたことになるのだった。
あとにも先にも、トットちゃんの話を、こんなにちゃんと聞いてくれた大人は、いなかった。
それにしても、まだ小学校一年生になったばかりのトットちゃんが、四時間も、ひとりでしゃべるぶんの話があったことは、ママや、前の学校の先生が聞いたら、きっと、びっくりするに違いないことだった。

were torn so she had to wear one Mother had bought. It had small dark red and gray checks and was made of jersey, and it wasn't bad, but Mother thought the red flowers embroidered on the collar were in bad taste. "Mother doesn't like the collar," said Totto-chan, holding it up for the headmaster to see.

After that, she could think of nothing more to say no matter how hard she tried. It made her rather sad. But just then the headmaster got up, placed his large, warm hand on her head, and said, "Well, now you're a pupil of this school."

Those were his very words. And at that moment Totto-chan felt she had met someone she really liked for the very first time in her life. You see, up till then, no one had ever listened to her for so long. And all that time the headmaster hadn't yawned once or looked bored, but seemed just as interested in what she had to say as she was.

Totto-chan hadn't learned how to tell time yet, but it did seem like a rather long time. If she had been able to, she would have been astonished, and even more grateful to the headmaster. For, you see, Mother and Totto-chan arrived at the school at eight, and when she had finished talking and the headmaster had told her she was a pupil of the school, he looked at his pocket watch and said, "Ah, it's time for lunch." So the headmaster must have listened to Totto-chan for four solid hours!

Neither before nor since did any grown-up listen to

このとき、トットちゃんは、まだ退学のことはもちろん、まわりの大人が、手こずってることも、気がついていなかったし、もともと性格も陽気で、忘れっぽいタチだったから、無邪気に見えた。でも、トットちゃんの中のどこかに、なんとなく、疎外感のような、他の子供と違って、ひとりだけ、ちょっと、冷たい目で見られているようなものを、おぼろげには感じていた。それが、この校長先生といると、安心で、暖かくて、気持ちがよかった。

(この人となら、ずーっと一緒にいてもいい)

これが、校長先生、小林宗作氏に、初めて逢った日、トットちゃんが感じた、感想だった。そして、有難いことに、校長先生も、トットちゃんと、同じ感想を、そのとき、持っていたのだった。

お弁当

トットちゃんは、校長先生に連れられて、みんなが、お弁当を食べるところを、見に行くことになった。お昼だけは、電車でなく、「みんな、講堂に集まることになっている」と校長先生が教えてくれた。講堂は、さっきトットちゃんが上がって来た石の階段の、つきあたりにあった。行ってみると、生徒たちが、大さわぎをしながら、机と椅子を、講堂に、まーるく輪になるように、並べているところだった。隅っこで、それを見ていたトットちゃんは、校長先生の上着をひっぱって聞いた。

「他の生徒は、どこにいるの?」

校長先生は答えた。

Totto-chan for as long as that. And, besides, it would have amazed Mother and her homeroom teacher to think that a seven-year-old child could find enough to talk about for four hours nonstop.

Totto-chan had no idea then, of course, that she had been expelled and that people were at their wit's end to know what to do. Having a naturally sunny disposition and being a bit absentminded gave her an air of innocence. But deep down she felt she was considered different from other children and slightly strange. The headmaster, however, made her feel safe and warm and happy. She wanted to stay with him forever.

That's how Totto-chan felt about Headmaster Sosaku Kobayashi that first day. And, luckily, the headmaster felt the same about her.

Lunchtime

The headmaster took Totto-chan to see where the children had lunch. "We don't have lunch in the train," he explained, "but in the Assembly Hall." The Assembly Hall was at the top of the stone steps Totto-chan had come up earlier. When they got there, they found the children noisily moving desks and chairs about, arranging them in a circle. As they stood in one corner and watched, Totto-chan tugged at the headmaster's jacket and asked, "Where are the rest of the children?"

"This is all there are," he replied.

「これで全部なんだよ」
「全部!?」
　トットちゃんは、信じられない気がした。だって、前の学校の一クラスと同じくらいしか、いないんだもの。そうすると、
「学校じゅうで、五十人くらいなの?」
　校長先生は、「そうだ」といった。トットちゃんは、なにもかも、前の学校と違ってると思った。
　みんなが着席すると、校長先生は、
「みんな、海のものと、山のもの、持って来たかい?」
　と聞いた。
「はーい」
　みんな、それぞれの、お弁当の、ふたを取った。
「どれどれ」
　校長先生は、机で出来た円の中に入ると、ひとりずつ、お弁当をのぞきながら、歩いている。生徒たちは、笑ったり、キイキイいったり、にぎやかだった。
「海のものと、山のもの、って、なんだろう」
　トットちゃんは、おかしくなった。でも、とっても、とっても、この学校は変わっていて、面白そう。お弁当の時間が、こんなに、愉快(ゆかい)で、楽しいなんて、知らなかった。トットちゃんは、明日からは、自分も、あの机にすわって、「海のものと、山のもの」のお弁当を、校長先生に見てもらうんだ、と思うと、もう、うれしさと、楽しみで、胸がいっぱいになり、叫びそうになった。
　お弁当を、のぞきこんでる校長先生の肩に、お昼の光が、やわらかく止まっていた。

"All there are?" Totto-chan couldn't believe it. There were as many children as this in just one grade at the other school.

"You mean there are only about fifty children in the whole school?"

"That's all," said the headmaster.

Everything about this school was different from the other one, thought Totto-chan.

When everyone was seated, the headmaster asked the pupils if they had all brought something from the ocean and something from the hills.

"Yes!" they chorused, opening their various lunch-boxes.

"Let's see what you've got," said the headmaster, strolling about in the circle of desks and looking into each box while the children squealed with delight.

"How funny," thought Totto-chan. "I wonder what he means by 'something from the ocean and something from the hills.' " This school was different. It was fun. She never thought lunch at school could be as much fun as this. The thought that tomorrow she would be sitting at one of those desks, showing the headmaster her lunch with "something from the ocean and something from the hills" made Totto-chan so happy she wanted to jump for joy.

As he inspected the lunchboxes, the headmaster's shoulders were bathed in the soft noontime light.

今日から学校に行く

きのう、『今日から、君は、もう、この学校の生徒だよ』そう校長先生にいわれたトットちゃんにとって、こんなに次の日が待ち遠しい、ってことは、今までになかった。だから、いつもなら朝、ママが叩き起こしても、まだベッドの上でボンヤリしてることの多いトットちゃんが、この日ばかりは、誰からも起こされない前に、もうソックスまではいて、ランドセルを背負って、みんなの起きるのを待っていた。

この家の中で、いちばん、きちんと時間を守るシェパードのロッキーは、トットちゃんの、いつもと違う行動に、けげんそうな目をむけながら、それでも、大きくのびをすると、トットちゃんにぴったりとくっついて、(なにか始まるらしい)ことを期待した。

ママは大変だった。大忙しで、『海のものと山のもの』のお弁当を作り、トットちゃんに朝御飯をたべさせ、毛糸で編んだヒモを通した、セルロイドの定期入れを、トットちゃんの首にかけた。これは定期を、なくさないためだった。パパは、

「いい子でね」

と頭をモシャモシャにしたままいった。

「もちろん!」

と、トットちゃんはいうと、玄関で靴をはき、戸をあけると、クルリと家の中をむき、ていねいにおじぎをして、こういった。

「みなさま、行ってまいります」

見送りに立っていたママは、ちょっと涙が出そうになった。それは、こんなに生き生きとしてお行儀よく、素直で、楽しそうにしてるトットちゃんが、つい、このあいだ、「退学になった」、ということを思い出したからだった。(新しい学校で、うまくいくといい……)ママは心からそう祈った。

ところが、次の瞬間、ママは、とび上がるほど驚いた。というのは、トットちゃんが、せっかくママが首からかけた定期を、ロ

Totto-chan Starts School

After the headmaster had said, "Now you're a pupil of this school," Totto-chan could hardly wait for the next day to dawn. She had never looked forward to a day so much. Mother usually had trouble getting Totto-chan out of bed in the morning, but that day she was up before anyone else, all dressed and waiting with her schoolbag strapped to her back.

The most punctual member of the household—Rocky, the German shepherd—viewed Totto-chan's unusual behavior with suspicion, but after a good stretch, he positioned himself close to her, expecting something to happen.

Mother had a lot to do. She busily made up a box lunch containing "something from the ocean and something from the hills" while she gave Totto-chan her breakfast. Mother also put Totto-chan's train pass in a plastic case and hung it around Totto-chan's neck on a cord so she wouldn't lose it.

"Be a good girl," said Daddy, his hair all tousled.

"Of course." Totto-chan put on her shoes and opened the front door, then turned around, bowed politely, and said, "Goodbye, everybody."

Tears welled up in Mother's eyes as she watched Totto-chan go out. It was hard to believe that this vivacious little girl, setting off so obediently and happily, had just been expelled from school. She prayed fervently that all would go well this time.

A moment later Mother was startled to see Totto-chan

ッキーの首にかけているのを見たからだった。ママは、(いったいどうなるのだろう?)と思ったけど、だまって、なりゆきを見ることにした。トットちゃんは、定期をロッキーの首にかけると、しゃがんで、ロッキーに、こういった。

「いい?　この定期のヒモは、あんたには、合わないのよ」

たしかに、ロッキーにはヒモが長く、定期は地面をひきずっていた。

「わかった?　これは私の定期で、あんたのじゃないから、あんたは電車に乗れないの。校長先生に聞いてみるけど。駅の人にも。で、『いい』っていったら、あんたも学校に来られるんだけど、どうかなあ」

ロッキーは、途中(とちゅう)までは、耳をピンと立てて神妙(しんみょう)に聞いていたけど、説明の終わりのところで、定期を、ちょっと、なめてみて、それから、あくびをした。それでも、トットちゃんは、一生懸命に話し続けた。

「電車の教室は、動かないから、お教室では、定期は要(い)らないと思うんだ。とにかく、今日は待ってるのよ」

たしかにロッキーは、いままで、歩いて通う学校の門まで、毎日、トットちゃんと一緒に行って、あとは、ひとりで家に帰って来ていたから、今日も、そのつもりでいた。

トットちゃんは、定期をロッキーの首からはずすと、たいせつそうに自分の首にかけると、パパとママに、もう一度、

「行ってまいりま〜す」

というと、今度はふり返らずに、ランドセルをカタカタいわせて走り出した。ロッキーも、からだをのびのびさせながら、並んで走り出した。

駅までの道は、前の学校に行く道と、ほとんど変わらなかった。だから、途中でトットちゃんは、顔見知りの犬や猫(ねこ)や、前の同級生と、すれ違った。トットちゃんは、そのたびに、

remove the train pass and hang it around Rocky's neck instead. "Oh dear . . ." thought Mother, but she decided to say nothing and wait and see what happened.

After Totto-chan put the cord with the pass around Rocky's neck, she squatted down and said to him, "You see? This pass doesn't fit you at all."

The cord was much too long and the pass dragged on the ground.

"Do you understand? This is my pass, not yours. You won't be able to get on the train. I'll ask the headmaster, though, and the man at the station, and see if they'll let you come to school, too."

Rocky listened attentively at first, ears pointed, but after giving the pass a few licks, he yawned. Totto-chan went on, "The classroom train doesn't move, so I don't think you'll need a ticket to get on that one, but today you'll just have to stay home and wait for me."

Rocky always used to walk with Totto-chan as far as the gate of the other school and then come back home. Naturally, he was expecting to do the same today.

Totto-chan took the cord with the pass off Rocky's neck and carefully hung it around her own. She called out once more to Mother and Daddy, "Goodbye!"

Then she ran off, without a backward glance, her bag flapping against her back. Rocky bounded along happily beside her.

The way to the station was almost the same as to the old school, so Totto-chan passed dogs and cats she knew, as well as children from her former class.

「定期を見せて、おどろかせてやろうかな？」
　と思ったけど、（もし遅(おそ)くなったら大変だから、今日は、よそう……）と決めて、どんどん歩いた。
　駅のところに来て、いつもなら左に行くトットちゃんが、右に曲がったので、可哀(かわい)そうにロッキーは、とても心配そうに立ち止まって、キョロキョロした。トットちゃんは、改札口のところまで行ったんだけど、もどって来て、まだ不思議そうな顔をしてるロッキーにいった。
「もう、前の学校には行かないのよ。新しい学校に行くんだから」
　それからトットちゃんは、ロッキーの顔に、自分の顔をくっつけ、ついでにロッキーの耳の中の、においをかいだ。（いつもと同じくらい、くさいけれど、私には、いい、におい！）そう思うと顔をはなして、
「バイバイ」
　というと、定期を駅の人に見せて、ちょっと高い駅の階段を、のぼり始めた。ロッキーは、小さい声で鳴いて、トットちゃんが階段を上がっていくのを、いつまでも見送っていた。

電車の教室

　トットちゃんが、きのう、校長先生から教えていただいた、自分の教室である、電車のドアに手をかけたとき、まだ校庭には、誰(だれ)の姿も見えなかった。今と違って、昔の電車は、外から開くように、ドアに取手がついていた。両手で、その取手を持って、右に引くと、ドアは、すぐ開いた。トットちゃんは、ドキドキしながら、そーっと、首をつっこんで、中を見てみた。
「わあーい!!」
　これなら、勉強しながら、いつも旅行をしてるみたいじゃない。

Should she show them her pass and impress them, Totto-chan wondered? But she didn't want to be late, so she decided not to that day, and hurried on.

When Totto-chan turned right at the station instead of left as usual, poor Rocky stopped and looked around anxiously. Totto-chan was already at the ticket gate, but she went back to Rocky, who stood, looking mystified.

"I'm not going to the other school any more. I'm going to a new one now."

Totto-chan put her face against Rocky's. His ears were smelly, as usual, but to Totto-chan it was a nice smell.

"Bye-bye," she said and, showing the man her pass, she started climbing up the steep station stairs. Rocky whimpered softly and watched until Totto-chan was out of sight.

The Classroom in the Train

No one had arrived yet when Totto-chan got to the door of the railroad car the headmaster had told her would be her classroom. It was an old-fashioned car, one that still had a door handle on the outside. You took hold of the handle with both hands and slid the door to the right. Totto-chan's heart was beating fast with excitement as she peeped inside.

"Ooh!"

網棚もあるし、窓も全部、そのままだし、違うところは、運転手さんの席のところに黒板があるのと、電車の長い腰かけを、はずして、生徒用の机と腰かけが進行方向にむいて並んでいるのと、つり革がないところだけ。あとは、天井も床も、全部、電車のままになっていた。トットちゃんは靴をぬいで中に入り、誰かの机のところに腰かけてみた。前の学校と、同じような木の椅子だったけど、それは、いつまでも腰かけていたいくらい、気持ちのいい椅子だった。トットちゃんは、うれしくて、（こんな気に入った学校は、絶対に、お休みなんかしないで、ずーっとくる）と、強く心に思った。

それからトットちゃんは、窓から外を見ていた。すると、動いていないはずの電車なのに、校庭の花や木が、少し風に揺れているせいか、電車が走っているような気持ちになった。

「ああ、うれしいなあ――」

トットちゃんは、とうとう声に出して、そう言った。それから、顔をぺったりガラス窓にくっつけると、いつも、うれしいとき、そうするように、デタラメ歌を、うたいはじめた。

とても　うれし
うれし　とても
どうしてかっていえば……

そこまで歌ったとき、誰かが乗りこんできた。女の子だった。その子は、ノートと筆箱をランドセルから出して机の上に置くと、背のびをして、網棚にランドセルをのせた。それから草履袋も、

Studying here would be like going on a perpetual journey. The windows still had baggage racks above them. The only difference was that there was a blackboard at the front of the car, and the lengthwise seats had been replaced by school desks and chairs all facing forward. The hand straps had gone, too, but everything else had been left just as it was. Totto-chan went in and sat down at someone's desk. The wooden chairs resembled those at the other school, but they were so much more comfortable she could sit on them all day. Totto-chan was so happy and liked the school so much, she made a firm decision to come to school every day and never take any holidays.

Totto-chan looked out of the window. She knew the train was stationary, but—was it because the flowers and trees in the school grounds were swaying slightly in the breeze?—it seemed to be moving.

"I'm so happy!" she finally said out loud. Then she pressed her face against the window and made up a song just as she always did whenever she was happy.

I'm so happy,
So happy am I!
Why am I happy?
Because . . .

Just at that moment someone got on. It was a girl. She took her notebook and pencil box out of her schoolbag and put them on her desk. Then she stood on tiptoe and put the bag on the rack. She put her shoe bag up there, too. Totto-chan stopped singing and

のせた。トットちゃんは歌をやめて、いそいで、まねをした。次に、男の子が乗ってきた。その子は、ドアのところから、バスケットボールのように、ランドセルを、網棚に投げこんだ。網棚の、網は、大きく波うつと、ランドセルを、投げ出した。ランドセルは、床に落ちた。その男の子は、「失敗！」というと、またもや、同じところから、網棚めがけて、投げこんだ。今度は、うまく、おさまった。「成功！」と、その子は叫ぶと、すぐ、「失敗！」といって、机によじのぼると、網棚のランドセルを開けて、筆箱やノートを出した。そういうのを出すのを忘れたから、失敗だったに違いなかった。

こうして、九人の生徒が、トットちゃんの電車に乗り込んで来て、それが、トモエ学園の、一年生の全員だった。

そしてそれは、同じ電車で旅をする、仲間だった。

授　業

お教室が本当の電車で、〝かわってる〟と思ったトットちゃんが、次に〝かわってる〟と思ったのは、教室で座(すわ)る場所だった。前の学校は、誰かさんは、どの机、隣(とな)りは誰、前は誰、と決まっていた。ところが、この学校は、どこでも、その日の気分や都合で、毎日、好きなところに座っていいのだった。

そこでトットちゃんは、さんざん考え、そして見回したあげく、朝、トットちゃんの次に教室に入って来た女の子の隣りに座ることに決めた。なぜなら、この子が、長い耳をした兎(うさぎ)の絵のついた、ジャンパー・スカートをはいていたからだった。

でも、なによりも〝かわっていた〟のは、この学校の、授業のやりかただった。

ふつうの学校は、一時間目が国語なら、国語をやって、二時間

quickly did the same. After that a boy got on. He stood at the door and threw his bag on the baggage rack as if he were playing basketball. It bounced off and fell on the floor. "Bad shot!" said the boy, taking aim again from the same place. This time it stayed on. "Nice shot!" he shouted, followed by "No, bad shot," as he scrambled onto the desk and opened his bag to get out his notebook and pencil box. His failure to do this first evidently made it count as a miss.

Eventually there were nine pupils in the car. They comprised the first grade at Tomoe Gakuen.

They would all be traveling together on the same train.

Lessons at Tomoe

Going to school in a railroad car seemed unusual enough, but the seating arrangements turned out to be unusual, too. At the other school each pupil was assigned a specific desk. But here they were allowed to sit anywhere they liked at any time.

After a lot of thought and a good look around, Totto-chan decided to sit next to the girl who had come after her that morning because the girl was wearing a pinafore dress with a long-eared rabbit on it.

The most unusual thing of all about this school, however, was the lessons themselves.

Schools normally schedule one subject, for example,

目が算数なら、算数、という風に、時間割の通りの順番なのだけど、この点、この学校は、まるっきり違っていた。

なにしろ、一時間目が始まるときに、その日、一日やる時間割の、全部の科目の問題を、女の先生が、黒板にいっぱいに書いちゃって、

「さあ、どれでも好きなのから、始めてください」

といったんだ。だから生徒は、国語であろうと、算数であろうと、自分の好きなのから始めていっこうに、かまわないのだった。だから、作文の好きな子が、作文を書いていると、うしろでは、物理の好きな子が、アルコール・ランプに火をつけて、フラスコをブクブクやったり、なにかを爆発(ばくはつ)させてる、なんていう光景は、どの教室でも見られることだった。この授業のやりかたは、上級になるに従って、その子供の興味を持っているもの、興味の持ちかた、物の考えかた、そして、個性、といったものが、先生に、はっきりわかってくるから、先生にとって、生徒を知る上で、何よりの勉強法だった。

また、生徒にとっても、好きな学科からやっていい、というのは、うれしいことだったし、嫌(きら)いな学科にしても、学校が終わる時間までに、やればいいのだから、なんとか、やりくり出来た。従って、自習の形式が多く、いよいよ、わからなくなってくると、先生のところに聞きに行くか、自分の席に先生に来ていただいて、納得(なっとく)のいくまで、教えてもらう。そして、例題をもらって、また自習に入る。これは本当の勉強だった。だから、先生の話や説明を、ボンヤリ聞く、といった事は、ないにひとしかった。

トットちゃんたち、一年生は、まだ自習をするほどの勉強を始めていなかったけど、それでも、自分の好きな科目から勉強する、ということには、かわりなかった。

カタカナを書く子。絵を描く子。本を読んでる子。中には、体操をしている子もいた。トットちゃんの隣りの女の子は、もう、

Japanese, the first period, when you just do Japanese; then, say, arithmetic the second period, when you just do arithmetic. But here it was quite different. At the beginning of the first period, the teacher made a list of all the problems and questions in the subjects to be studied that day. Then she would say, "Now, start with any of these you like."

So whether you started on Japanese or arithmetic or something else didn't matter at all. Someone who liked composition might be writing something, while behind you someone who liked physics might be boiling something in a flask over an alcohol burner, so that a small explosion was liable to occur in any of the classrooms.

This method of teaching enabled the teachers to observe—as the children progressed to higher grades—what they were interested in as well as their way of thinking and their character. It was an ideal way for teachers to really get to know their pupils.

As for the pupils, they loved being able to start with their favorite subject, and the fact that they had all day to cope with the subjects they disliked meant they could usually manage them somehow. So study was mostly independent, with pupils free to go and consult the teacher whenever necessary. The teacher would come to them, too, if they wanted, and explain any problem until it was thoroughly understood. Then pupils would be given further exercises to work at alone. It was study in the truest sense of the word, and it meant there were no pupils just sitting inattentively

ひらがなが書けるらしく、ノートに写していた。トットちゃんは、なにもかもが珍しくて、ワクワクしちゃって、みんなみたいに、すぐ勉強、というわけにはいかなかった。

そんなとき、トットちゃんの後ろの机の男の子が立ち上がって、黒板のほうに歩き出した。ノートを持って。黒板の横の机で、他の子に何かを教えている先生のところに行くらしかった。その子の歩くのを、後ろから見たトットちゃんは、それまでキョロキョロしてた動作をピタリと止めて、ほおづえをつき、じーっと、その子を見つめた。その子は、歩くとき、足をひきずっていた。とっても、歩くとき、からだがゆれた。初めは、わざとしているのか、と思ったくらいだった。でも、やっぱり、わざとじゃなくて、そういう風になっちゃうんだ、と、しばらく見ていたトットちゃんにわかった。

その子が、自分の机にもどって来るのを、トットちゃんは、さっきの、ほおづえのまま、見た。目と目が合った。その男の子は、トットちゃんを見ると、ニコリと笑った。トットちゃんも、あわてて、ニコリとした。その子が、後ろの席に座ると、——座るのも、他の子より、時間がかかったんだけど——トットちゃんは、クルリと振りむいて、その子に聞いた。

「どして、そんな風に歩くの?」

その子は、やさしい声で静かに答えた。とても利口そうな声だった。

while the teacher talked and explained.

The first grade pupils hadn't quite reached the stage of independent study, but even they were allowed to start with any subject they wanted.

Some copied letters of the alphabet, some drew pictures, some read books, and some even did calisthenics. The girl next to Totto-chan already knew all her alphabet and was writing it into her notebook. It was all so unfamiliar that Totto-chan was a bit nervous and unsure what to do.

Just then the boy sitting behind her got up and walked toward the blackboard with his notebook, apparently to consult the teacher. She sat at a desk beside the blackboard and was explaining something to another pupil. Totto-chan stopped looking around the room and, with her chin cupped in her hands, fixed her eyes on his back as he walked. The boy dragged his leg, and his whole body swayed dreadfully. Totto-chan wondered at first if he was doing it on purpose, but she soon realized the boy couldn't help it.

Totto-chan went on watching him as the boy came back to his desk. Their eyes met. The boy smiled.

「僕、小児麻痺（しょうにまひ）なんだ」
「しょうにまひ?」
　トットちゃんは、それまで、そういう言葉を聞いたことがなかったから、聞き返した。その子は、少し小さい声でいった。
「そう、小児麻痺。足だけじゃないよ。手だって……」
　そういうと、その子は、長い指と指が、くっついて、曲がったみたいになった手を出した。トットちゃんは、その左手を見ながら、
「なおらないの?」
　と心配になって聞いた。その子は、だまっていた。トットちゃんは、悪いことを聞いたのかと悲しくなった。すると、その子は、明るい声でいった。
「僕の名前は、やまもとやすあき。君は?」
　トットちゃんは、その子が元気な声を出したので、うれしくなって、大きな声でいった。
「トットちゃんよ」
　こうして、山本泰明ちゃんと、トットちゃんのお友達づきあいが始まった。
　電車の中は、暖かい日差しで、暑いくらいだった。誰かが、窓を開けた。新しい春の風が、電車の中を通り抜け、子供たちの髪（かみ）の毛が歌っているように、とびはねた。
　トットちゃんの、トモエでの第一日目は、こんな風に始まったのだった。

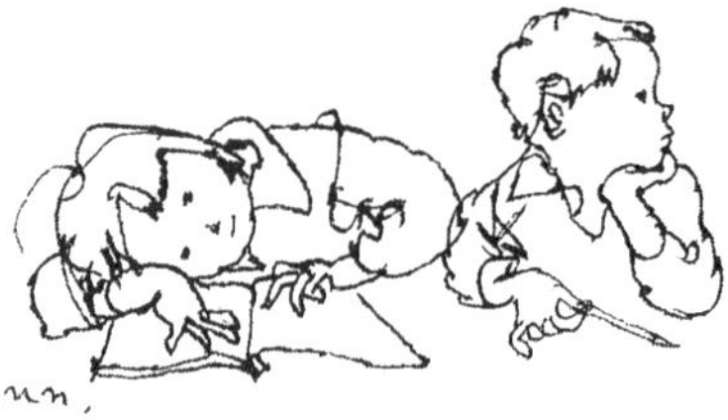

Totto-chan hurriedly smiled back. When he sat down at the desk behind her—it took him longer than other children to sit down—she turned around and asked, "Why do you walk like that?"

He replied quietly, with a gentle voice that sounded intelligent, "I had polio."

"Polio?" Totto-chan repeated, never having heard the word before.

"Yes, polio," he whispered. "It's not only my leg, but my hand, too." He held it out. Totto-chan looked at his left hand. His long fingers were bent and looked as if they were stuck together.

"Can't they do anything about it?" she asked, concerned. He didn't reply, and Totto-chan became embarrassed, wishing she hadn't asked. But the boy said brightly, "My name's Yasuaki Yamamoto. What's yours?"

She was so glad to hear him speak in such a cheerful voice that she replied loudly, "I'm Totto-chan."

That's how Yasuaki Yamamoto and Totto-chan became friends.

The sun made it quite hot inside the train. Someone opened a window. The fresh spring breeze blew through the car and tossed the children's hair about with carefree abandon.

In this way Totto-chan's first day at Tomoe began.

海のものと山のもの

さて、トットちゃんが待ちに待った『海のものと山のもの』のお弁当の時間が来た。この『海のものと山のもの』って、なにか、といえば、それは、校長先生が考えた、お弁当のおかずのことだった。ふつうなら、お弁当のおかずについて、「子供が好き嫌いをしないように、工夫してください」とか、「栄養が、片寄らないようにお願いします」とか、いうところだけど、校長先生はひとこと、

「海のものと、山のものを持たせてください」

と、子供たちの家の人に、頼んだ、というわけだった。

山は……例えば、お野菜とか、お肉とか（お肉は山でとれるってわけじゃないけど、大きく分けると、牛とか豚とかニワトリとかは、陸に住んでいるのだから、山のほうに入るって考え）海は、お魚とか、佃煮とか。この二種類を、必ずお弁当のおかずに入れてほしい、というのだった。

（こんなに簡単に、必要なことを表現できる大人は、校長先生の他には、そういない）とトットちゃんのママは、ひどく感心していた。しかも、ママにとっても、海と山とに、わけてもらっただけで、おかずを考えるのが、とても面倒なことじゃなく思えてきたから、不思議だった。それに校長先生は、海と山といっても、〝無理しないこと〟〝ぜいたくしないこと〟といってくださったから、山は〝キンピラゴボウと玉子焼〟で海は〝おかか〟という風でよかったし、もっと簡単な海と山を例にすれば、〝おのりと梅干し〟でよかったのだ。

そして子供たちは、トットちゃんが初めて見た時に、とっても、うらやましく思ったように、お弁当の時間に、校長先生が、自分たちのお弁当箱の中をのぞいて、

「海のものと、山のものは、あるかい?」

と、ひとりずつ確かめてくださるのが、うれしかったし、それから、自分たちも、どれが海で、どれが山かを発見するのも、も

Sea Food and Land Food

Now it was time for "something from the ocean and something from the hills," the lunch hour Totto-chan had looked forward to so eagerly.

The headmaster had adopted the phrase to describe a balanced meal—the kind of food he expected you to bring for lunch in addition to your rice. Instead of the usual "Train your children to eat everything," and "Please see that they bring a nutritiously balanced lunch," this headmaster asked parents to include in their children's lunchboxes "something from the ocean and something from the hills."

"Something from the ocean" meant sea food—things such as fish and *tsukuda-ni* (tiny crustaceans and the like boiled in soy sauce and sweet saké), while "something from the hills" meant, for instance, vegetables and meat. You don't necessarily find meat in the hills, but since cattle and pigs and chickens live on the land, he included them in the hills category.

Mother was very impressed by this and thought that few headmasters were capable of expressing such an important rule so simply. Oddly enough, just having to choose from two categories made preparing lunch seem simpler. And besides, the headmaster pointed out that one did not have to think too hard or be extravagant to fulfill the two requirements. The land food could be just *kinpira gobō* (spicy burdock) or an omelette, and the sea food merely flakes of dried bonito. Or simpler still, you could have *nori* (a kind of seaweed) for

のすごいスリルだった。

でも、たまには、母親が忙しかったり、あれこれ手がまわらなくて、山だけだったり、海だけという子もいた。そういうときは、どうなるのか、といえば、その子は心配しないでいいのだった。なぜなら、お弁当の中をのぞいて歩く校長先生の後ろから、白い、かっぽうまえかけをかけた、校長先生の奥さんが、両手に、おなべをひとつずつ持って、ついて歩いていた。そして先生が、どっちか足りない子の前で、

「海！」

というと、奥さんは、海のおなべから、ちくわの煮たのを、二個くらい、お弁当箱のふたに、のせてくださったし、先生が、

「山！」

といえば、もう片ほうの、山のおなべから、おいもの煮ころがしが、とび出す、という風だったから。

こんなわけだったので、どの子供たちも、「ちくわが嫌い」なんて、そんなことは、いわなかったし、（誰のおかずが上等で、誰のおかずが、いつも、みっともない）なんて思わなくて、海と山とが揃った、ということが、うれしくて、お互いに笑いあったり、叫んだりするのだった。

トットちゃんにも、やっと、『海のものと山のもの』が、なんだかわかった。そしたら、（ママが、今朝、大急行で作ってくれたお弁当は、大丈夫かな？）と少し心配になった。でも、ふたをとった

"ocean" and a pickled plum for "hills."

Just as the day before, when Totto-chan had watched so enviously, the headmaster came and looked in all the lunchboxes.

"Have you something from the ocean and something from the hills?" he asked, checking each one. It was so exciting to discover what each had brought from the ocean and from the hills.

Sometimes a mother had been too busy and her child had only something from the hills, or only something from the ocean. But never mind. As the headmaster made his round of inspection, his wife followed him, wearing a cook's white apron and holding a pan in each hand. If the headmaster stopped in front of a pupil saying, "Ocean," she would dole out a couple of boiled *chikuwa* (fish rolls) from the "Ocean" saucepan, and if the headmaster said, "Hills," out would come some chunks of soy-simmered potato from the "Hills" saucepan.

No one would have dreamed of saying, "I don't like fish rolls," any more than thinking what a fine lunch so-and-so has or what a miserable lunch poor so-and-so always brings. The children's only concern was whether they had satisfied the two requirements—the ocean and the hills—and if so their joy was complete and they were all in good spirits.

Beginning to understand what "something from the ocean and something from the hills" was all about, Totto-chan had doubts whether the lunch her mother had so hastily prepared that morning would be

とき、トットちゃんが、
「わあーい」
といいそうになって、口を押(おさ)えたくらい、それは、それは、ステキなお弁当だった。黄色のいり卵、グリンピース、茶色のデンブ、ピンク色の、タラコをパラパラに炒(い)ったの、そんな、いろんな色が、お花畑みたいな模様になっていたのだもの。
校長先生は、トットちゃんのを、のぞきこむと、
「きれいだね」
といった。トットちゃんは、うれしくなって、
「ママは、とっても、おかず上手(じょうず)なの」
といった。校長先生は、
「そうかい」
といってから、茶色のデンブを指して、トットちゃんに、
「これは、海かい？　山かい？」
と聞いた。トットちゃんは、デンブを、ジーっと見て、
「これは、どっちだろう」
と考えた。（色からすると、山みたいだけど。だって、土みたいな色だからさ。でも……わかんない）そう思ったので、
「わかりません」
と答えた。すると、校長先生は、大きな声で、
「デンブは、海と山と、どっちだい？」
と、みんなに聞いた。ちょっと考える間があって、みんな一斉(いっせい)に、「山！」とか、「海！」とか叫んで、どっちとも決まらなかった。みんなが叫び終わると、校長先生は、いった。
「いいかい、デンブは、海だよ」
「なんで」
と、肥(ふと)った男の子が聞いた。校長先生は、机の輪のまん中に立つと、
「デンブは、魚の身をほぐして、細かくして、炒って作ったもの

approved. But when she opened the lunchbox, she found such a marvelous lunch inside, it was all she could do to stop herself shouting, "Oh, goody, goody!"

Totto-chan's lunch contained bright yellow scrambled eggs, green peas, brown *denbu*, and pink flaked cod roe. It was as colorful as a flower garden.

"How very pretty," said the headmaster.

Totto-chan was thrilled. "Mother's a very good cook," she said.

"She is, is she?" said the headmaster. Then he pointed to the *denbu*. "All right. What's this? Is it from the ocean or the hills?"

Totto-chan looked at it, wondering which was right. It was the color of earth, so maybe it was from the hills. But she couldn't be sure.

"I don't know," she said.

The headmaster then addressed the whole school, "Where does *denbu* come from, the ocean or the hills?"

After a pause, while they thought about it, some shouted, "Hills," and others shouted, "Ocean," but no one seemed to know for certain.

"All right. I'll tell you," said the headmaster. "*Denbu* is from the ocean."

"Why?" asked a fat boy.

Standing in the middle of the circle of desks, the headmaster explained, "*Denbu* is made by scraping the flesh of cooked fish off the bones, lightly roasting it and crushing it into fine pieces, which are then dried and flavored."

だからさ」
　と説明した。
「ふーん」
　と、みんなは、感心した声を出した。そのとき誰かが、
「先生、トットちゃんのデンブ、見てもいい?」
　と聞いた。校長先生が、
「いいよ」
　というと、学校中の子が、ゾロゾロ立って来て、トットちゃんのデンブを見た。デンブは知ってて、食べたことはあっても、いまの話で、急に興味が出てきた子も、また、自分の家のデンブと、トットちゃんのと、少し、かわっているのかな?　と思って、見たい子もいるに違いなかった。デンブを見にきた子の中には、においをかぐ子もいたので、トットちゃんは、鼻息で、デンブが飛ばないか、と心配になったくらいだった。
　でも、初めてのお弁当の時間は、少しドキドキはしたけど、楽しくて、『海のものと山のもの』を考えるのも面白いし、デンブがお魚ってわかったし、ママは、『海のものと山のもの』を、ちゃんと入れてくれたし、トットちゃんは、(ぜんぶ、よかったな)と、うれしくなった。そして、次に、うれしいのは、ママのお弁当は、たべると、おいしいことだった。

よく噛めよ

　で、ふつうなら、これで、「いただきまーす」になるんだけど、このトモエ学園は、ここで、合唱が入るのが、また、かわっていた。校長先生は、音楽家でもあったから、『お弁当をたべる前に歌う歌』というのを作った。ただし、これは、作曲が、イギリス人で、歌詞だけが、校長先生だった。というより、本当は、もとも

"Oh!" said the children, impressed. Then someone asked if they could see Totto-chan's *denbu*.

"Certainly," said the headmaster, and the whole school trooped over to look at Totto-chan's *denbu*. There must have been children who knew what *denbu* was but whose interest had been aroused, as well as those who wanted to see if Totto-chan's *denbu* was any different from the kind they had at home. So many children sniffed at Totto-chan's *denbu* that she was afraid the bits might get blown away.

Totto-chan was a little nervous that first day at lunch, but it was fun. It was fascinating wondering what was sea food and what was land food, and she learned that *denbu* was made of fish, and Mother had remembered to include something from the ocean and something from the hills, so all in all everything had been all right, she thought contentedly.

And the next thing that made Totto-chan happy was that when she started to eat the lunch Mother had made, it was delicious.

"Chew It Well!"

Normally one starts a meal by saying, "*Itadakimasu*" (I gratefully partake), but another thing that was different at Tomoe Gakuen was that first of all everybody sang a song. The headmaster was a musician and he had made up a special "Song to Sing before Lunch."

とあった曲に、先生が替え歌をつけた、というのが、正しいのだけれど。もともとの曲は、あの有名な、『船をこげよ (Row Your Boat)』

〽ロー　ロー　ロー　ユアー　ボート
ジェントリー　ダウン　ザ　ストゥリーム
メリリー　メリリー　メリリー　メリリー
ライフ　イズ　バット　ア　ドリーム

で、これに校長先生がつけた歌詞は、次のようだった。

〽よーく　噛めよ
たべものを
噛めよ　噛めよ　噛めよ　噛めよ
たべものを

そして、これを歌い終わると、初めて、「いただきまーす」になるのだった。〝ロー　ロー　ロー　ユアー　ボート〟のメロディーに、〝よーく　噛めよ〟は、ぴったりとあった。だから、この学校の卒業生は、随分と大きくなるまで、このメロディーは、お弁当の前に歌う歌だ、と信じていたくらいだった。校長先生は、自分の歯が抜けていたので、この歌を作ったのかもしれないけど、本当は、「よく噛めよ」というより、お食事は、時間をかけて、楽しく、いろんなお話をしながら、ゆっくり食べるものだ、と、いつも生徒に話していたから、そのことを忘れないように、この歌を作ったのかもしれなかった。さて、みんなは、大き

Actually, he just made up the words and set them to the tune of the well-known English round "Row, Row, Row Your Boat."

Row, row, row your boat
Gently down the stream;
Merrily, merrily, merrily, merrily,
Life is but a dream.

The words the headmaster made up went like this:

Chew, chew, chew it well,
Everything you eat;
Chew it and chew it and chew it and chew it,
Your rice and fish and meat!

It wasn't until they had finished singing this song that the children all said "*Itadakimasu.*"

The words fitted the tune of "Row, Row, Row Your Boat" so well that even years later many of the pupils firmly believed it had always been a song you sang before eating.

The headmaster may have made up the song because he had lost some of his teeth, but he was always telling the children to eat slowly and take plenty of time over meals while enjoying pleasant conversation, so it is more likely he made up this song to remind them of that.

After they had sung the song at the tops of their

な声で、この歌を歌うと、「いただきまーす」といって、海のものと山のものに、とりかかった。トットちゃんも、もちろん、同じようにした。
講堂は、一瞬だけ、静かになった。

散　歩

お弁当のあと、みんなと校庭で走りまわったトットちゃんが、電車の教室にもどると、女の先生が、
「みなさん、今日は、とてもよく勉強したから、午後は、なにをしたい?」
と聞いた。トットちゃんが、(えーと、私のしたいこと、っていえば……)なんて考えるより前に、みんなが口々に、
「散歩!」
といった。すると先生は、
「じゃ、行きましょう」
といって立ち上がり、みんなも、電車のドアを開けて、靴をはいて、とび出した。トットちゃんは、パパや犬のロッキーと、散歩に行ったことはあるけど、学校で、散歩に行く、って知らなかったから、びっくりした。でも、散歩は大好きだから、トットちゃんも、急いで靴をはいた。
あとでわかったことだけど、先生が朝の一時間目に、その日、一日やる時間割の問題を黒板に書いて、みんなが、頑張って、午前中に、全部やっちゃうと、午後は、たいがい散歩になるのだった。これは一年生でも、六年生でも同じだった。
学校の門を出ると、女の先生を、まん中にして、九人の一年生は、小さい川に沿って歩き出した。川の両側には、ついこの間まで満開だった、桜の大きい木が、ずーっと並んでいた。そして見渡

voices, the children all said "*Itadakimasu*" and settled down to "something from the ocean and something from the hills."

For a while the Assembly Hall was quiet.

School Walks

After lunch Totto-chan played in the school grounds with the others before returning to the classroom, where the teacher was waiting for them.

"You all worked hard this morning," she said, "so what would you like to do this afternoon?"

Before Totto-chan could even begin to think about what she wanted to do, there was an unanimous shout.

"A walk!"

"All right," said the teacher, and the children all began rushing to the doors and dashing out. Totto-chan used to go for walks with Daddy and Rocky, but she had never heard of a school walk and was astounded. She loved walks, however, so she could hardly wait.

As she was to find out later, if they worked hard in the morning and completed all the tasks the teacher had listed on the blackboard, they were generally allowed to go for a walk in the afternoon. It was the same whether you were in the first grade or the sixth grade.

Out of the gate they went—all nine first grade pupils

す限り、菜の花畑だった。今では、川も埋めたてられ、団地やお店でギュウヅメの自由が丘も、この頃は、ほとんどが畠だった。
「お散歩は、九品仏よ」
　と、兎の絵のジャンパー・スカートの、女の子がいった。この子は、〝サッコちゃん〟という名前だった。それからサッコちゃんは、
「九品仏の池のそばで、この前、蛇を見たわよ」とか、「九品仏のお寺の古い井戸の中に、流れ星が落ちてるんだって」
　とか教えてくれた。みんなは、勝手に、おしゃべりしながら歩いていく。空は青く、蝶々が、いっぱい、あっちにも、こっちにも、ヒラヒラしていた。
　十分くらい歩いたところで、女の先生は、足を止めた。そして、黄色い菜の花を指して、
「これは、菜の花ね。どうして、お花が咲くか、わかる?」
　といった。そして、それから、メシベとオシベの話をした。生徒は、みんな道にしゃがんで、菜の花を観察した。先生は、蝶々も、花を咲かせるお手伝いをしている、といった。本当に、蝶々は、お手伝いをしているらしく、忙しそうだった。
　それから、また先生は歩き出したから、みんなも、観察はおしまいにして、立ち上がった。誰かが、
「オシベと、アカンベは違うよね」

with their teacher in their midst—and began walking along the edge of a stream. Both banks of the stream were lined with large cherry trees that had only recently been in full bloom. Fields of yellow mustard flowers stretched as far as the eye could see. The stream has long since disappeared, and apartment buildings and stores now crowd the area. But in those days Jiyugaoka was mostly fields.

"We go as far as Kuhonbutsu Temple," said the girl with the rabbit on her pinafore dress. Her name was Sakko-chan.

"We saw a snake by the pond there last time," said Sakko-chan. "There's an old well in the temple grounds which they say a shooting star fell into once."

The children chatted away about anything they liked as they walked along. The sky was blue and the air was filled with the fluttering of butterflies.

After they had walked for about ten minutes, the teacher stopped. She pointed to some yellow flowers, and said, "Look at these mustard flowers. Do you know why flowers bloom?"

She explained about pistils and stamens while the children crouched by the road and examined the flowers. The teacher told them how butterflies helped flowers bloom. And, indeed, the butterflies seemed very busy helping.

Then the teacher set off again, so the children stopped inspecting the flowers and stood up. Someone said, "They don't look like pistols, do they?"

とか、いった。トットちゃんは、(違うんじゃないかなあ!)と思ったけど、よく、わかんなかった。でも、オシベとメシベが大切、ってことは、みんなと同じように、よくわかった。

そして、また十分くらい歩くと、こんもりした小さな森が見えてきて、それが九品仏のお寺だった。

境内に入ると、みんな、見たいもののほうに、キャアキャアいって走っていった。サッコちゃんが、

「流れ星の井戸を見に行かない?」

といったので、もちろん、トットちゃんは、

「うん」

といって、サッコちゃんの後ろについて走った。井戸っていっても、石みたいので出来ていて、二人の胸のところくらいまであり、木のフタがしてあった。二人でフタを取って、下をのぞくと中は真暗で、よく見ると、コンクリートの固まりか、石の固まりみたいのが入っているだけで、トットちゃんが想像してたみたいな、キラキラ光る星は、どこにも見えなかった。長いこと、頭を井戸の中につっこんでいたトットちゃんは、頭をあげると、サッコちゃんに聞いた。

「お星さま、見た?」

サッコちゃんは、頭をふると、

「一度も、ないの」

といった。トットちゃんは、どうして光らないか、を考えた。そして、いった。

「お星さま、いま、寝てるんじゃないの?」

サッコちゃんは、大きい目を、もっと大きくしていった。

「お星さまって、寝るの?」

トットちゃんは、あまり確信がなかったから、早口でいった。

「お星さまは、昼間、寝てて、夜、起きて、光るんじゃないか、って思うんだ」

Totto-chan didn't think so either, but like the other children, she was sure that pistils and stamens were very important.

After they had walked for about another ten minutes, a thickly wooded park came into view. It surrounded the temple called Kuhonbutsu. As they entered the grounds the children scattered in various directions.

"Want to see the shooting-star well?" asked Sakko-chan, and naturally Totto-chan agreed and ran after her.

The well looked as if it was made of stone and came up to their chests. It had a wooden lid. They lifted the lid and peered in. It was pitch dark, and Totto-chan could see something like a lump of concrete or stone, but nothing whatsoever resembling the twinkling star she had imagined. After staring inside for a long time, she asked, "Have you seen the star?"

Sakko-chan shook her head. "No, never."

Totto-chan wondered why it didn't shine. After thinking about it for a while, she said, "Maybe it's asleep."

Opening her big round eyes even wider, Sakko-chan asked, "Do stars sleep?"

"I think they must sleep in the daytime and then wake up at night and shine," said Totto-chan quickly because she wasn't really sure.

Then the children gathered together and walked around the temple grounds. They laughed at the bare bellies of the two Deva Kings that stood on either side

それから、みんなで、仁王さまのお腹を見て笑ったり、薄暗いお堂の中の仏さまを、（少し、こわい）と思いながらも、のぞいたり、天狗さまの大きな足跡の残ってる石に、自分の足をのせてくらべてみたり、池のまわりをまわって、ボートに乗ってる人に、「こんちは」といったり、お墓のまわりの、黒いツルツルの、あぶら石を借りて、石けりをしたり、もう満足するぐらい、遊んだ。特に、初めてのトットちゃんは、もう興奮して、次から次と、なにかを発見しては、叫び声をあげた。

春の陽差しが、少し傾いた。先生は、

「帰りましょう」

といって、また、みんな、菜の花と桜の木の間の道を、並んで、学校にむかった。

子供たちにとって、自由で、お遊びの時間と見える、この『散歩』が、実は、貴重な、理科や、歴史や、生物の勉強になっているのだ、ということを、子供たちは気がついていなかった。

トットちゃんは、もう、すっかり、みんなと友達になっていて、前から、ずーっと一緒にいるような気になっていた。だから、帰り道に、

「明日も、散歩にしよう！」

と、みんなに大きい声でいった。みんなは、とびはねながら、いった。

「そうしよう」

蝶々は、まだまだ忙しそうで、鳥の声が、近くや遠くに聞こえていた。

トットちゃんの胸は、なんか、うれしいもので、いっぱいだった。

of the gate, guarding the temple, and gazed with awe at the statue of Buddha in the semidarkness of the Main Hall. They placed their feet in the great footprint in a stone said to have been made by a Tengu—a long-nosed goblin. They strolled around the pond, calling out "Hello!" to the people in rowboats. And they played hopscotch to their hearts' content with the glossy black pebbles around the graves. Everything was new to Totto-chan, and she greeted each discovery with an excited shout.

"Time to go back!" said the teacher, as the sun began to dip, and the children set off for the school along the road between the mustard blossoms and the cherry trees.

Little did the children realize then that these walks—a time of freedom and play for them—were in reality precious lessons in science, history, and biology.

Totto-chan had already made friends with all the children and felt she had known them all her life.

"Let's go for a walk again tomorrow!" she shouted to them all on the way back.

"Yes, let's!" they shouted back, hopping and skipping.

The butterflies were still going busily about their business, and the song of birds filled the air. Totto-chan's heart was bursting with joy.

夏休みが始まった

「明日、テントを張って、野宿をします。毛布とパジャマを持って、夕方、学校に来てください」

　こういう校長先生からの手紙を、トットちゃんは、学校から持って帰って、ママに見せた。明日から、夏休み、という日のことだった。

「野宿って、なあに?」

　トットちゃんは、ママに聞いた。ママも、考えていたところだったけど、こんなふうに答えた。

「どっか、外にテントを張って、その中に寝るんじゃないの?　テントだと、寝ながら、星とかお月様が見られるのよ。でも、どこにテントを張るのかしらね。交通費っていうのがないから、きっと学校の近くよ」

　その夜、ベッドに入っても、トットちゃんは、野宿のことを考えると、ちょっと、こわいみたいな、物凄く冒険みたいな、なんかドキドキする気持ちで、いつまでも、ねむくならなかった。

　次の日、目が覚めると、もう、トットちゃんは、荷物を作り始めた。そして、パジャマを入れたリュックの上に、毛布をのせてもらうと、少し、つぶされそうになりながら、夕方、ママとパパにバイバイをすると、出かけていった。

　学校にみんなが集まると、校長先生は、

「みんな講堂においで」

　といい、みんなが講堂に集まると、小さなステージの上に、ゴワゴワしたものを、持って上がった。それは、グリーン色のテントだった。先生は、それを広げると、いった。

「これから、テントの張りかたを教えるから、よく見てるんだよ」

　そして、先生は、一人で、〝ふんふん〟いいながら、あっちの

Summer Vacation Begins

"We are going camping tomorrow. Please come to the school in the evening with blankets and pajamas," said the note from the headmaster that Totto-chan took home and showed to Mother. Summer vacation began the following day.

"What does camping mean?" asked Totto-chan.

Mother was wondering, too, but she replied, "Doesn't it mean you're probably going to put up tents somewhere outdoors and sleep in them? Sleeping in a tent you can see the moon and the stars. I wonder where they'll set up the tents. There's no mention of fares so it's probably somewhere near the school."

That night, after Totto-chan had gone to bed, she couldn't get to sleep for ages. The idea of going camping sounded rather scary—a tremendous adventure—and her heart beat very fast.

The following morning she started packing as soon as she woke up. But that evening, as her blanket was placed on top of the knapsack that held her pajamas and she said goodbye and set off, she felt very small and frightened.

When the children were gathered at the school, the headmaster said, "Now then, all of you, come to the Assembly Hall." When they got there he went up onto the small stage carrying something stiff and starchy. It was a green tent.

"I'm going to show you how to pitch a tent," he said, spreading it out. "Please watch carefully."

紐（ひも）をひっぱったり、こっちに柱を建てたりして、あっ、という間に、とてもステキな三角形のテントを張ってしまった。そして、いった。

「いいかい。これから君たちは、みんなで講堂に、たくさん、テントを張って、野宿だ！」

ママは、たいがいの人が考えるように、外にテントを張るのだと思ったのだけれど、校長先生の考えは、違っていた。

〝講堂なら、雨が降っても、少々、夜中に寒くなっても、大丈夫！〟

子供たちは、一斉に、「野宿だ！　野宿だ！」と叫びながら、何人かずつ、組になり、先生たちにも手伝ってもらって、とうとう、講堂の床に、みんなの分だけのテントを張ってしまった。一つのテントは、三人くらいずつ寝られる大きさだった。トットちゃんは、はやばやと、パジャマになると、あっちのテント、こっちのテントと、入口から、はいずって、出たり入ったり、満足のいくまでした。みんなも同じように、よそのテントを訪問しあった。

全部が、パジャマになると、校長先生は、みんなが見える、まん中にすわって、先生が旅をした外国の話をしてくれた。

子供たちは、テントから首を半分だした寝ころんだ形や、きちんと、すわったり、上級生の膝（ひざ）に、頭をもたせかけたりしながら、

All alone, puffing and blowing, he pulled ropes this way and set up poles that way, and before you could say "Jack Robinson," there stood a beautiful tent!

"Come on, then," he said. "Now you're going to set up tents all over the Assembly Hall and start camping."

Mother imagined, as anyone would have, that they would put up the tents outdoors, but the headmaster had other ideas. In the Assembly Hall the children would be all right even if it rained in the night or got a bit cold.

With delighted shouts of "We're camping, we're camping!" the children divided into groups, and, with the help of the teachers, they finally managed to set up the required number of tents. One tent could sleep about three children. Totto-chan quickly got into her pajamas, and soon children were happily crawling in and out of this tent and that one. There was much visiting to and fro.

When everyone was in pajamas, the headmaster sat down in the middle where they could all see him and talked to them about his travels abroad.

Some of the children lay in their tents with just their heads showing, while others sat up properly, and some lay with their heads on older children's laps, all listening to his tales of foreign countries they had never seen and sometimes never even heard of. The headmaster's stories were fascinating, and at times they felt as if the children described in lands across the sea were friends.

行ったことは勿論、それまで見たことも、聞いたこともない外国の話を聞いた。先生の話は珍しく、ときには、海のむこうの子供たちが、友達のように思えるときも、あった。

そして、たったこれだけのことが……、講堂にテントを張って、寝ることが……子供たちにとっては、一生、忘れることの出来ない、楽しくて、貴重な経験になった。校長先生は、確実に、子供のよろこぶことを知っていた。

先生の話が終わり、講堂の電気が消えると、みんなは、ゴソゴソと、自分のテントの中に入った。

あっちのテントからは、笑い声が……、こっちのテントからは、ヒソヒソ声が、それから、むこうのテントでは、とっくみ合いが……。それも段々と静かになっていった。

星も月もない野宿だったけど、心の底から満足した子供たちが、小さい講堂で、野宿をしていた。

そして、その夜、たくさんの星と、月の光は、講堂を包むように、いつまでも、光っていたのだった。

大冒険

講堂での野宿の次の次の日、とうとう、トットちゃんの大冒険の日が来た。それは、泰明ちゃんとの約束だった。そして、その約束は、ママにもパパにも、泰明ちゃんの家の人にも、秘密だった。その約束が、どういうのか、というと、それは、「トットちゃんの木に、泰明ちゃんを招待する」というものだった。トットちゃんの木、といっても、それはトモエの校庭にある木で、トモエの生徒は、校庭のあっちこっちに自分専用の、登る木を決めてあったので、トットちゃんのその木も、校庭のはしっこの、九品仏に行く細い道に面した垣根のところに生えていた。その木は、太

And so it happened that this simple event—sleeping in tents in the Assembly Hall—became for the children a happy and valuable experience they would never forget. The headmaster certainly knew how to make children happy.

When the headmaster finished speaking and the lights in the Assembly Hall had been turned out, all the children went into their own tents. Laughter could be heard from some; whispers from others; while from a tent at the far end came the sound of a scuffle. Gradually silence fell.

It was camping without any moon or stars, but the children enjoyed it thoroughly. To them that little Assembly Hall seemed like a real camping ground, and memory wrapped that night in moonbeams and starlight forever.

The Great Adventure

Two days after they camped in the Assembly Hall, the day of Totto-chan's great adventure finally came to pass. It was the day of her appointment with Yasuaki-chan. And it was a secret that neither Mother nor Daddy nor Yasuaki-chan's parents knew. She had invited Yasuaki-chan to her tree.

The students at Tomoe each had a tree in the school grounds they considered their own climbing tree. Totto-chan's tree was at the edge of the grounds near

くて、登るときツルツルしていたけど、うまく、よじ登ると、下から二メートルくらいのところが、二股（ふたまた）になっていて、その、またのところが、ハンモックのように、ゆったりとしていた。トットちゃんは、学校の休み時間や、放課後、よく、そこに腰をかけて、遠くを見物したり、空を見たり、道を通る人たちを眺めたりしていた。

そんなわけで、よその子の木に登らせてほしいときは、

「御免（ごめん）くださいませ。ちょっとお邪魔（じゃま）します」

という風にいって、よじ登らせてもらうくらい、〝自分の木〟って、決まっていた。

でも、泰明ちゃんは、小児麻痺（しょうにまひ）だったから、木に登ったことがなく、自分の木も、決めてなかった。だから、今日、トットちゃんは、その自分の木に、泰明ちゃんを招待しようと決めて、泰明ちゃんと、約束してあったのだ。トットちゃんが、みんなに秘密にしたのは、きっと、みんなが反対するだろう、と思ったからだった。トットちゃんは、家を出るとき、

「田園調布（でんえんちょうふ）の、泰明ちゃんの家に行く」

とママにいった。嘘（うそ）をついてるので、なるべくママの顔を見ないで、靴（くつ）の紐（ひも）のほうを見るようにした。でも、駅までついて来たロッキーには、別れるとき、本当のことを話した。

「泰明ちゃんを、私の木に登らせてあげるんだ！」

トットちゃんが、首から紐でさげた定期をバタバタさせて学校につくと、泰明ちゃんは、夏休みで誰もいない校庭の、花壇のそばに立っていた。泰明ちゃんは、トットちゃんより、一歳（さい）、年上だったけど、いつも、ずーっと大きい子のように話した。

泰明ちゃんは、トットちゃんを見つけると、足をひきずりながら、手を前のほうに出すような恰好（かっこう）で、トットちゃんのほうに走って来た。トットちゃんは、誰にも秘密の冒険をするのだ、と思うと、もう嬉（うれ）しくなって、泰明ちゃんの顔を見て、

the fence beside the lane leading to Kuhonbutsu. It was a large tree and slippery to climb, but if you climbed it skillfully you could get to a fork about six feet from the ground. The fork was as comfortable as a hammock. Totto-chan used to go there during recess and after school and sit and look off into the distance or up at the sky, or watch the people going by below.

The children considered "their" trees their own private property, so if you wanted to climb someone else's tree you had to ask their permission very politely, saying, "Excuse me, may I come in?"

Because Yasuaki-chan had had polio he had never climbed a tree, and couldn't claim one as his own. That's why Totto-chan decided to invite him to her tree. They kept it a secret because they thought people were sure to make a fuss if they knew.

When she left home, Totto-chan told her mother she was going to visit Yasuaki-chan at his home in Denenchofu. She was telling a lie, so she tried not to look at Mother but kept her eyes on her shoelaces. But Rocky followed her to the station, so when they parted company, she told him the truth.

"I'm going to let Yasuaki-chan climb my tree!" she said.

When Totto-chan reached the school, her train pass flapping around her neck, she found Yasuaki-chan waiting by the flower beds in the grounds that were deserted now that it was summer vacation. He was only a year older than Totto-chan, but he always sounded much older when he spoke.

「ヒヒヒヒヒ」

　と笑った。泰明ちゃんも、笑った。それからトットちゃんは、自分の木のところに、泰明ちゃんを連れて行くと、ゆうべから考えていたように、用務員の小父さんの物置に走っていって、立てかける梯子を、ズルズルひっぱって来て、それを、木の二股あたりに立てかけると、どんどん登って、上で、それを押さえて、

「いいわよ、登ってみて?」

　と下をむいて叫んだ。でも泰明ちゃんは、手や足の力がなかったから、とても一人では、一段目も登れそうになかった。そこで、トットちゃんは、物凄い早さで、後ろむきになって梯子を降りると、今度は、泰明ちゃんのお尻を後ろから押して、上にのせようとした。ところが、トットちゃんは、小さくて、やせている子だったから、泰明ちゃんのお尻を押さえるだけが精いっぱいで、グラグラ動く梯子を押さえる力は、とてもなかった。泰明ちゃんは、梯子にかけた足を降ろすと、だまって、下を向いて、梯子のところに立っていた。トットちゃんは、思っていたより、難しいことだったことに、初めて気がついた。

When Yasuaki-chan saw Totto-chan, he hurried toward her, dragging his leg and holding his arms out in front to steady himself. Totto-chan was thrilled to think they were going to do something secret, and she giggled. Yasuaki-chan giggled, too.

Totto-chan led Yasuaki-chan to her tree, and then, just as she had thought it out the night before, she ran to the janitor's shed and got a ladder, which she dragged over to the tree and leaned against the trunk so that it reached the fork. She climbed up quickly and, holding the top of the ladder, called down, "All right, try climbing up!"

Yasuaki-chan's arms and legs were so weak it seemed he could not even get on the first rung without help. So Totto-chan hurried down the ladder backward and tried pushing Yasuaki-chan up from behind. But Totto-chan was so small and slender that it was all she could do to hold onto Yasuaki-chan, let alone keep the ladder steady. Yasuaki-chan took his foot off the bottom rung and stood beside the ladder, his head bowed. Totto-chan realized for the first time that it was going to be more difficult than she had thought. What should she do?

She wanted so badly to have Yasuaki-chan climb her tree, and he had been looking forward to it so much. She went around and faced him. He looked so disconsolate that she puffed out her cheeks and made a funny face to cheer him up.

"Wait! I've got an idea!"

She ran back to the janitor's shed and pulled out one

（どうしよう……）
　でも、どんなことをしても、泰明ちゃんも楽しみにしている、この自分の木に、登らせたかった。トットちゃんは、悲しそうにしている泰明ちゃんの顔の前にまわると、頬っぺたをふくらませた面白い顔をしてから、元気な声でいった。
「待ってて？　いい考えがあるんだ!!」
　それから、また物置まで走って行き、なにか、（いい考えのものはないか）と、いろいろなものを、次々と引っ張り出してみた。そして、とうとう、脚立を発見した。
（これなら、グラグラしないから、押さえなくても大丈夫）
　それから、トットちゃんは、その脚立を、ひきずって来た。それまで、「こんなに自分が力持ちって知らなかった」と思うほどの凄い力だった。脚立を立ててみると、ほとんど、木の二股のあたりまで、とどいた。それから、トットちゃんは、泰明ちゃんのお姉さんみたいな声でいった。
「いい？　こわくないのよ。もう、グラグラしないんだから」
　泰明ちゃんは、とてもビクビクした目で脚立を見た。それから、汗びっしょりのトットちゃんを見た。泰明ちゃんも、汗ビッショリだった。それから、泰明ちゃんは、木を見上げた。そして心を決めたように、一段目に足をかけた。
　それから、脚立の一番上まで、泰明ちゃんが登るのに、どれくらいの時間がかかったか、二人にもわからなかった。夏の日射しの照りつける中で、二人とも、何も考えていなかった。とにかく、泰明ちゃんが、脚立の上まで登れればいい、それだけだった。トットちゃんは、泰明ちゃんの足の下にもぐっては、足を持ち上げ、頭で泰明ちゃんのお尻を支えた。泰明ちゃんも、力の入る限り頑張って、とうとう、てっぺんまで、よじ登った。
「ばんざい！」
　ところが、それから先が絶望的だった。二股に飛びうつったト

thing after another to see if she could find something that would help. She finally discovered a stepladder. It would remain steady so she wouldn't have to hold it.

She dragged the stepladder over, amazed at her own strength, and was delighted to find that it almost reached the fork.

"Now, don't be afraid," she said in a big-sisterly voice. "This isn't going to wobble."

Yasuaki-chan looked nervously at the stepladder. Then he looked at Totto-chan, drenched in perspiration. Yasuaki-chan was sweating profusely, too. He looked up at the tree. Then, with determination, he placed a foot on the first rung.

Neither of them was conscious of the time it took Yasuaki-chan to reach the top of the stepladder. The hot summer sun beat down, but they had no thoughts for anything except getting Yasuaki-chan to the top of the stepladder. Totto-chan got underneath him and lifted his feet up while steadying his bottom with her head. Yasuaki-chan struggled with all his might, and finally reached the top.

"Hooray!"

But from there it was hopeless. Totto-chan jumped onto the fork, but no matter how she tried, she couldn't get Yasuaki-chan onto the tree from the stepladder. Clutching the stepladder Yasuaki-chan looked at Totto-chan. She suddenly felt like crying. She had wanted so badly to invite Yasuaki-chan onto her tree and show him all sorts of things.

ットちゃんが、どんなに引っ張っても、脚立の泰明ちゃんは、木の上に移れそうもなかった。脚立の上につかまりながら、泰明ちゃんは、トットちゃんを見た。突然、トットちゃんは、泣きたくなった。

（こんなはずじゃなかった。私の木に泰明ちゃんを招待して、いろんなものを見せてあげたいと思ったのに……）

　でも、トットちゃんは、泣かなかった。もし、トットちゃんが泣いたら、泰明ちゃんも、きっと泣いちゃう、と思ったからだった。

　トットちゃんは、泰明ちゃんの、小児麻痺で指がくっついたままの手を取った。トットちゃんの手より、ずーっと指が長くて、大きい手だった。トットちゃんは、その手を、しばらく握っていた。そして、それから、いった。

「寝る恰好になってみて？　ひっぱってみる」

　このとき、脚立の上に腹ばいになった泰明ちゃんを、二股の上に立ち上がって、ひっぱり始めたトットちゃんを、もし、大人が見たら、きっと悲鳴をあげたに違いない。それくらい、二人は、不安定な恰好になっていた。

　でも、泰明ちゃんは、もう、トットちゃんを信頼していた。そして、トットちゃんは、自分の全生命を、このとき、かけていた。小さい手に、泰明ちゃんの手を、しっかりとつかんで、ありったけの力で、泰明ちゃんを、引っ張った。

　入道雲が、時々、強い日射しを、さえぎってくれた。

　そして、ついに、二人は、木の上で、むかいあうことが出来たのだった。トットちゃんは、汗で、ビチャビチャの横わけの髪の毛を、手でなでつけながら、おじぎをしていった。

「いらっしゃいませ」

　泰明ちゃんは、木に、よりかかった形で、少し恥ずかしそうに笑いながら、答えた。

But she didn't cry. She was afraid that if she did, Yasuaki-chan might start crying, too.

Instead she took hold of his hand, with its fingers all stuck together because of the polio. It was bigger than hers and his fingers were longer. She held his hand for a long time. Then she said, "Lie down and I'll try and pull you over."

If any grown-ups had seen her standing on the fork of the tree starting to pull Yasuaki-chan—who was lying on his stomach on the stepladder—onto the tree, they would have let out a scream. It must have looked terribly precarious.

But Yasuaki-chan trusted Totto-chan completely. And Totto-chan was risking her life for him. With her tiny hands clutching his, she pulled with all her might. From time to time a large cloud would mercifully protect them from the blistering sun.

「お邪魔します」
　泰明ちゃんにとっては、初めて見る景色だった。そして、
「木に登るって、こういうのか、って、わかった」
　って、うれしそうにいった。
　それから、二人は、ずーっと木の上で、いろんな話をした。泰明ちゃんは、熱をこめて、こんな話もした。
「アメリカにいる、お姉さんから、聞いたんだけど、アメリカに、テレビジョンていうのが出来たんだって。それが日本に来れば、家にいて、国技館の、お相撲が見られるんだって。箱みたいな形だって」
　遠くに行くのが大変な泰明ちゃんにとって、家にいて、いろんなものが見られることが、どんなに、うれしいことか、それは、まだトットちゃんには、わからないことだった。だから、
『箱の中から、お相撲が出るなんて、どういう事かな？　お相撲さんて、大きいのに、どうやって、家まで来て、箱の中に入るのかな？』
　と考えたけど、とっても、変わってる話だとは、思った。まだ、誰もテレビジョンなんて知らない時代のことだった。トットちゃんに、最初にテレビの話を教えてくれたのは、この泰明ちゃんだった。
　セミが、ほうぼうで鳴いていた。
　二人とも、満足していた。
　そして、泰明ちゃんにとっては、これが、最初で、最後の、木登りになってしまったのだった。

At long last, the two stood face to face on the tree. Brushing her damp hair back, Totto-chan bowed politely and said, "Welcome to my tree."

Yasuaki-chan leaned against the trunk smiling rather bashfully. He said, "May I come in?"

Yasuaki-chan was able to see vistas he had never glimpsed before. "So this is what it's like to climb a tree," he said happily.

They stayed on the tree for a long time and talked about all sorts of things.

"My sister in America says they've got something there called television," said Yasuaki-chan with enthusiasm. "She says that when it comes to Japan we'll be able to sit at home and watch sumo wrestling. She says it's like a box."

Totto-chan didn't understand yet how much it would mean to Yasuaki-chan, who couldn't go very far afield, to be able to watch all sorts of things at home.

She simply wondered how sumo wrestlers could get inside a box in your own house. Sumo wrestlers were so big! But it was fascinating all the same. In those days nobody knew about television. Yasuaki-chan was the first to tell Totto-chan about it.

The cicadas were singing and the two children were so happy. And for Yasuaki-chan it was the first and last time he ever climbed a tree.

一番わるい洋服

校長先生は、トモエの生徒の父兄に、

「一番わるい洋服を着せて、学校に寄こしてください」

と、いつもいっていた。というのは、〝汚したら、お母さんに叱られる〟とか、〝破けるから、みんなと遊ばない〟ということは、子供にとって、とてもつまらないことだから、どんなに泥んこになっても、破けても、かまわない、一番わるい洋服を着させてください、というお願いだった。トモエの近くの小学校には、制服を着てる子もいたし、セーラー服とか、学生服に半ズボン、という服装もあった。だけど、トモエの子は、本当に普段着で学校に来た。そして先生のお許しがあるわけだから、洋服のことを気にしないで、もう出来るだけ遊んだ。でも今のように、ジーンズなど丈夫な布地のない時代だったから、どの子のズボンも、つぎがあたっていたし、女の子のスカートも、出来るだけ、丈夫な布で作ってあった。

トットちゃんの、もっとも大好きな遊びは、よその家の垣根や、原っぱの垣根の下をくぐることだったから、洋服のことを考えなくていいのは、都合がよかった。その頃の垣根は、子供たちが「テツジョウモウ（鉄条網）」と呼んでいる有刺鉄線というか、バラ線

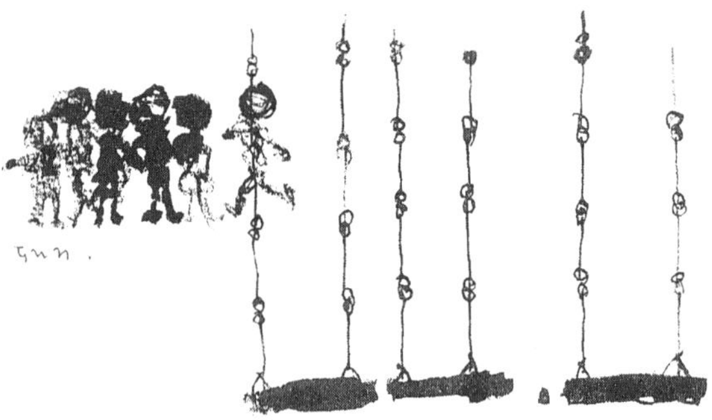

Their Worst Clothes

The headmaster was always asking parents to send their children to school at Tomoe in their worst clothes. He wanted them to wear their worst clothes so that it wouldn't matter if they got muddy and torn. He thought it a shame for children to worry about being scolded if their clothes got dirty or to hesitate joining in some game because their clothes might get torn. There were elementary schools near Tomoe where the girls were dressed in sailor-suit uniforms and the boys wore high-collared jackets with shorts. The Tomoe children came to school in their ordinary clothes, and they had their teachers' permission to play to their hearts' content without giving their clothes a thought. Trousers in those days weren't made of anything durable like today's jeans, so all the boys had patches on their trousers and the girls wore skirts or dresses made of the strongest material available.

Totto-chan's favorite pastime was crawling under the fences of other people's gardens and vacant lots, so it suited her very well not to have to think about her clothes. There were a lot of barbed-wire fences in those days, and some of them had wire right down to ground level. In order to get under one like that you had to burrow like a dog. No matter how careful she was, Totto-chan would always manage to catch her dress on the barbs and tear it. Once, when she had on an old muslin dress that was really quite threadbare, she didn't just tear it or catch it, the whole thing got shredded

が、柵のまわりに張りめぐらしてあるのが多かった。中には、地面につくくらい下のほうまで、しっかり、からんでいるのもよくあった。これに、どうやってもぐりこむか、といえば、この垣根の下に頭をつっこんで、テツジョウモウを押しあげ、穴を掘って、もぐる、ちょうど、犬と同じやりかただった。そしてこのとき、トットちゃんも、気をつけてはいるのだけれど、どうしても、トゲトゲの鉄線に洋服がひっかかって、破けてしまうのだった。いつかなどは、かなり古くて、「しょう」の抜けているメリンス風の布地のワンピースを着てる時だったけど、このときは、スカートが破ける、とか、ひっかかった、というのじゃなく、背中からお尻にかけて、七ヵ所くらい、ジャキジャキに破けて、どうみても、背中にハタキを背負ってる、という風になってしまった。古いけど、ママが、この洋服を気に入ってる、と知っているトットちゃんは、一生懸命に考えた。つまり、「テツジョウモウをもぐってて破けた」といっては、ママに気の毒だから、なんか嘘をついてでも、

「どうしても破けるのは仕方がなかった」

という風に説明したほうがいい、と考えたのだった。やっと思いついた嘘を、家に帰るなり、トットちゃんは、ママにいった。

「さっきさ、道歩いてたら、よその子が、みんなで、私の背中にナイフ投げたから、こんなに破けたの」

いいながら、（ママが、いろいろ、くわしく聞いたら困るな）と思っていた。ところが、うれしいことに、ママは、

「あら、そう、大変だったわね」

といっただけだった。（ああ、よかった）と、トットちゃんは安心して、（これなら、ママの好きな洋服が破れたのも仕方がなかった……って、ママにもわかってもらえた）と思った。

勿論、ママはナイフで破けたなんて話を信じたわけではなかった。だいたい、後ろからナイフを背中に投げて、体に怪我もしないで、洋服だけビリビリになるなんてことは、あり得なかったし、

from top to bottom and hung from her shoulders in strips. Although it was old, she knew Mother was very fond of that dress, so Totto-chan racked her brains about what to say. She hadn't the heart to tell Mother she had torn it on barbed wire. She thought it would be better to think up a lie that would make it sound as if she couldn't help tearing it. She finally hit on the following story.

"As I was walking along the road," she lied, on arriving home, " a lot of children I didn't know threw knives at my back. That's why my dress got torn like this." But as she spoke she wondered how to answer further questions her mother might ask.

Thankfully, all her mother said was, "It must have been awful!"

Totto-chan heaved a sigh of relief. Mother obviously realized that under those circumstances she couldn't help getting Mother's favorite dress torn.

Naturally, Mother didn't believe her story about the knives. Knives thrown at her back would have injured her as well as tearing her dress, and Totto-chan didn't seem at all frightened by the incident. Mother realized at once it was a fabrication. However, it was unusual for Totto-chan to go to such lengths to make up an excuse. She realized Totto-chan must have felt badly about the dress and that pleased her. But there was something Mother had wanted to know for some time, and this seemed a good opportunity to find out.

"I can see how your dresses can get torn by knives

第一、トットちゃんが、全然、こわかった、という風でもないのだから、すぐ嘘とわかった。でも、なんとなく、トットちゃんにしては、いいわけをするなんて、いつもと違うから、きっと洋服のことを気にしてるに違いない、と考え、(いい子だわ)と思った。ただ、ママは、前から聞きたい、と思っていたことを、この際、トットちゃんに聞いてみようと思って、いった。

「洋服が、ナイフとか、いろんなもので破けるのは、わかるけど、どうして、パンツまで、毎日、毎日、ジャキジャキになるの?」

木綿のレースなんかがついているゴム入りの白いパンツのお尻のあたりが、毎日、破けているのが、ママには、ちょっとわからなかった。

(パンツが泥んことか、すれてる程度なら、おすべりとか、しりもちとかで、そうなった、とわかるけど、ビリビリになるのは、どうしてかしら?)

トットちゃんは、少し考えてからいった。

「だってさ、もぐるときは、絶対、はじめはスカートがひっかかっちゃうんだけど、出るときはお尻からで、そいで、垣根のはじっこから、ずーっと、〝ごめんくださいませ〟と〝では、さようなら〟をやるから、パンツなんか、すぐ破けちゃうんだ!」

なんだかわかんないけど、ママは、おかしくなった。

「それで、それは面白いの?」

ママの質問に、トットちゃんは、びっくりした様な顔で、ママを見て、いった。

「ママだって、やってみれば?　絶対に面白いから。でさ、ママだって、パンツ破けちゃうと思うんだ!?」

トットちゃんが、どんなにスリルがあって楽しいか、という遊びは、こうだった。

つまり、テツジョウモウの張ってある長い空地の垣根を見つけると、はじのほうから、トゲトゲを持ちあげ、穴を掘って中にも

and things like that," said Mother, "but how do you manage to tear your panties too, day after day?"

Mother could never understand how Totto-chan's lace-trimmed panties got torn every day around the rear. She could see how panties could get muddy and worn thin by going down slides or falling on one's bottom, but how did they get torn to shreds?

Totto-chan thought about it for a while, then said, "You see, when you burrow under a fence you can't help catching your skirt as you go through, and your panties when you back out, and you have to do an 'Excuse me, may I come in?' and a 'Well, goodbye then' from one end of the fence to the other, so your panties and things are bound to tear."

Mother didn't really understand, but it sounded rather amusing.

"Is it fun?" she asked.

"Why don't you try it?" said Totto-chan, astonished at the question. "It's great fun and you'll tear your panties, too!"

The game that Totto-chan liked so much and found so thrilling went like this.

First you had to find a large vacant lot surrounded by a barbed-wire fence. "Excuse me, may I come in?" consisted of lifting up the spiked wire, digging a hole, and crawling under. Once inside you lifted up a neighboring bit of barbed wire and dug another hole, this time backing out saying, "Well, goodbye then." It finally became quite clear even to Mother how Totto-chan's

ぐりこむのが、まず「ごめんくださいませ」で、次に、いま、もぐった、ちょっと隣りのトゲトゲを、今度は、中から持ちあげ、また穴を掘って、このときは、「では、さようなら」といって、お尻から出る。このとき、つまりお尻から出るときに、スカートがまくれて、パンツがテツジョウモウにひっかかるのだ、と、ママにも、やっとわかった。こんな風に、次々と、穴を掘り、スカートやパンツもひっかけながら、「ごめんくださいませ」そして、「では、さようなら」をくり返す。つまり上から見ていたら、垣根の、はしからはしまで、ジグザグに、入ったり出たりするのだから、パンツも破けるわけだった。
（それにしても、大人なら、疲れるだけで、なにが面白いか、と思えるこういうことが、子供にとっては、本当に楽しいことなんだから、なんて、うらやましいこと……）。ママは、髪の毛は勿論、爪や耳の中まで泥だらけのトットちゃんを見ながら思った。そして、校長先生の、「汚してもかまわない洋服」の提案は、本当に子供のことを、よくわかっている大人の考えだ、といつものことだけど、ママは感心したのだった。

「それからさあー」

　ふだんでも、みんなが楽しみにしてる、トモエのお弁当の時間に、最近になって、面白いことが、また増えた。
　トモエのお弁当の時間は、今までは、校長先生が、全校生徒五十人の「海のもの」と「山のもの」の、おかずの点検があって、その海か山か、どっちかが、足りないとわかった子に、校長先生の奥さんが、両手にひとつずつ持って歩いている海と山の、お鍋（なべ）から、おかずが配られて、それから、〽よく噛（か）めよ、たべものを

skirt got drawn up as she backed out causing her panties to catch on the barbed wire. The process would be repeated over and over again—burrowing under the wire with an "Excuse me, may I come in?" and then backing out through a fresh hole with a "Well, goodbye then," tearing skirt and panties every time. Totto-chan happily zigzagged back and forth burrowing under the barbed-wire fence from one end to the other. No wonder her panties got torn.

To think that a game like that, which would only tire a grown-up and not be amusing at all, could be such fun to a child! Watching Totto-chan, with dirt in her hair and fingernails and even in her ears, Mother couldn't help feeling a little envious. And she couldn't help admiring the headmaster. His suggestion that the children wear clothes they could get as dirty as they liked was just another example of how well he understood them.

"And Then . . . Uh . . ."

Lunchtime at Tomoe had always been fun, but lately a new interest had been added.

The headmaster still inspected the lunchboxes of all fifty pupils to see if they had "something from the ocean and something from the hills"—and his wife with her two saucepans was ready to supply the missing elements from anyone's lunch—after which they would

……を、みんなで歌って、
「いただきまーす」
　になったのだけど、今度から、この「いただきまーす」のあとに、
「誰かさんの、〝おはなし〟」
　というのが入ることになったのだ。
　このあいだ、校長先生が、
「みんな、もっと話が上手になったほうが、いいな。どうだい、今度から、お弁当の時、みんなが喰(た)べてる間、毎日、違う誰かさんが、ひとり、みんなの輪のまん中に入って、お話する、ってのは?」
　といった。子供たちは、(自分で話すのは上手じゃないけど、聞くのは面白いな)とか、(わあー、みんなにお話してあげるのなんか、スッゴク好き)とか、いろんなふうに考えた。トットちゃんは、(どんなお話をすればいいか、まだわかんないけど、やってみる!)と思った。
　こんなわけで、ほとんどが校長先生の考えに賛成だったので、次の日から、この「おはなし」が始まったのだった。
　校長先生は、自分の外国生活の経験から、ふつう、日本では「ごはんの時は、だまって喰べなさい」と、家でいわれている子供たちに、
「食事というのは、出来るだけ楽しく。だから、急いで喰べないで、時間をかけて、お弁当の時間には、いろんな話をしながら喰べていい」
　といつもいっていた。そして、もうひとつ、
(これからの子供は、人の前に出て、自分の考えを、はっきりと自由に、恥ずかしがらずに表現できるようになることが、絶対に必要だ)
　と考えていたから、そろそろ始めてみよう、と決めたのだった。だから、校長先生は、みんなが、
「賛成!」

all sing "Chew, chew, chew it well, Everything you eat," followed by, "I gratefully partake." But from now on, after "I gratefully partake," someone had to give a little talk.

One day the headmaster said, "I think we all ought to learn how to speak better. What do you think? After this, while we are eating our lunch, let's have somebody different each day stand in the middle of the circle and tell us about something. How about that?"

Some children thought they weren't very good at speaking, but it would be fun to listen to others. Some thought it would be super to tell people things they knew. Totto-chan didn't know what she would talk about but was willing to give it a try. Most of the children were in favor of the idea so they decided to start the talks the next day.

Japanese children are usually taught at home not to talk at mealtimes. But as a result of his experience abroad, the headmaster used to encourage his pupils to take plenty of time over their meals and enjoy conversation.

Besides that, he thought it was essential for them to learn how to get up in front of people and express their ideas clearly and freely without being embarrassed, so he decided it was time to put this theory into practice.

After the children had agreed to the idea, this is what he told them. Totto-chan listened attentively.

"You needn't worry about trying to be a good speaker," he said. "And you can talk about anything

といったとき、こういった。トットちゃんは一生懸命に聞いた。
「いいかい。上手にお話しようとか、そんなふうに思わなくていいんだよ。そして話も、自分のしたいこと、なんでもいいからね。とにかく、やってみようじゃないか?」
なんとなく順番も決まった。お話をする番になった人だけは、〽よく噛めよ……を歌ったら、一人だけ、いそいで喰べていいことも決まった。
ところが、三人ぐらいとかの、小さいグループの中で、休み時間に話すのと違って、全校生徒、五十人のまん中で、話す、というのは、勇気もいるし、むずかしいことだった。初めの頃は、照れちゃって、ただ「イヒイヒイヒイヒ」笑ってばかりの子や、必死になって考えて来たのに、出たとたんに忘れちゃって、話の題名らしい、
「蛙の横っちょ飛び」
というのだけを何回も、くり返したあげく、結局、
「雨が降ると……、おしまい」
といって、おじぎをして席に帰る子もいた。
トットちゃんは、まだ番が来なかったけど、来たら、やっぱり、自分の一番好きな、「お姫さまと王子さま」の話にしよう、と決めていた。でも、トットちゃんの「お姫さまと王子さま」の話は有名で、いつもお休みの時間にしてあげると、みんなが、「もう飽きたよ」というぐらいだったけど、やっぱり、それにしよう、と思っていた。

こうやって、毎日、かわりばんこに前に出て話す習慣が少しずつついて来た、ある日、絶対に順番

you like. You can talk about things you'd like to do. Anything. At any rate, let's give it a try."

The order of speakers was decided upon. And it was also decided that whoever was going to speak that day would eat lunch quickly, straight away after the song was over.

The children soon discovered that unlike talking to two or three friends during lunch hour, standing up in the middle of the whole school needed a good deal of courage and was quite difficult. Some children were so shy at first that they just giggled. One boy had gone to a lot of effort and prepared a talk only to forget all of it the moment he stood up. He repeated several times his fine-sounding title, "Why Frogs Jump Sideways," then started off with, "When it rains . . ." but got no further. Finally he said, "That's all," bowed, and went back to his seat.

Totto-chan's turn hadn't come yet, but she decided that when it did she would tell her favorite story, "The Prince and the Princess." Everyone knew it, and whenever she wanted to tell it during breaks, the children would say, "We're tired of that one." But all the same, she decided, that was the story she was going to tell.

The new scheme was beginning to work rather well when, one day, the child whose turn it was to give a talk firmly refused.

"I have nothing to say," the boy declared.

Totto-chan was amazed to think that anyone could possibly have nothing to say. But that boy just didn't.

が来ても、「しない」といいはる子がいた。それは、
「話は、なんにも無い！」
　という男の子だった。トットちゃんは、（話なんか無い）という子がいたことに、とても、びっくりした。ところが、その子は、無い！　のだった。校長先生は、その子の空になったお弁当箱の、のった机の前にいくと、いった。
「君は話が、無いのかあ……」
「なんにも無い！」
　その子は、いった。決して、ひねくれたり、抵抗してるんじゃなくて、本当に無いようだった。校長先生は、
「ハ、ハ、ハ、ハ」
　と歯の抜けているのを気にしないで笑って、それからいった。
「じゃ、作ろうじゃないか！」
「作るの？」
　その子は、びっくりしたようにいった。
　それから校長先生は、その子を、みんなのすわってる輪のまん中に立たすと、自分は、その子の席にすわった。そして、いった。
「君が、今朝、起きてから、学校に来るまでのことを、思い出してごらん！　最初に、なにをした？」
　その男の子は、頭の毛をボリボリ掻きながら、まず、
「えーと」
　といった。そしたら校長先生がいった。
「ほら、君は、『えーと』っていったよ。話すこと、あったじゃないか。『えーと』の次は、どうした？」
　すると、その子は、また頭をボリボリ掻きながら、
「えーと、朝起きた」
　といった。トットちゃんやみんなは、少し、おかしくなったけど、注目していた。それから、その子は、
「そいでさあー」

The headmaster went over to the boy's desk with its empty lunchbox.

"So you have nothing to say," he said.

"Nothing."

The boy wasn't trying to be clever, or anything like that. He honestly couldn't think of anything to talk about.

The headmaster threw back his head and laughed, heedless of the gaps in his teeth.

"Let's try and find you something to say."

"Find me something?" The boy seemed startled.

The headmaster got the boy to stand in the center of the ring while he sat down at the boy's desk.

"Try and remember," he said, "what you did this morning after you got up and before you came to school. What did you do first?"

"Well," said the boy and then just scratched his head.

"Fine," said the headmaster, "You've said, 'Well.' You did have something to say. What did you do after 'well?' "

"Well, . . . uh . . . I got up," he said, scratching his head some more.

Totto-chan and the others were amused, but listened attentively. The boy went on, "Then, uh . . ." He scratched his head again. The headmaster sat patiently watching the boy, with a smile on his face and his hands clasped on the desk. Then he said, "That's splendid. That will do. You got up this morning. You've made everyone understand that. You don't have to be

といって、また、頭をボリボリやった。先生は、じーっと、その子の様子を、ニコニコした顔で、手を机の上に組んで見ていたけど、そのとき、いった。

「いいんだよ、それで。君が朝起きた、ってことが、これで、みんなにわかったんだから。面白いことや、笑わせること話したから偉(えら)いっていうことじゃないんだ。『話が無い！』っていった君が、話を見つけたことが、大切なんだよ」

するとその子は、凄(すご)く大きな声で、こういった。

「それからさあー」

みんなは、いっせいに身をのり出した。その子は、大きく息を吸うと、いった。

「それからさあー、お母さんがさあー、歯をみがきなさい、っていったから、みがいた」

校長先生は拍手した。みんなも、した。すると、その子は、前よりも、もっと大きい声で、いった。

「それからさあー」

みんなは拍手をやめ、もっと耳を澄(す)ませて、ますます身をのり出した。その子は、得意そうな顔になって、いった。

「それからさあー、学校に来た！」

身をのり出した上級生の中には、少しつんのめったのか、お弁当箱に、頭をぶつける子もいた。でも、みんなは、とてもうれしくなった。

（あの子に、話があった！）

先生は大きく拍手をした。トットちゃんたちも、うんとした。まん中に立ってる「それからさあー」の子も、一緒になって、拍手をした。講堂は、拍手だらけになった。

この拍手のことを、この子は、恐らく大人になっても、忘れないに違いなかった。

amusing or make people laugh to be a good speaker. The important thing is that you said you hadn't anything to talk about and you did find something to say."

But the boy didn't sit down. He said in a very loud voice, "And then . . . uh . . ."

All the children leaned forward. The boy took a deep breath and went on, "And then . . . uh . . . Mother . . . uh . . . she said, 'Brush your teeth' . . . uh . . . so I brushed my teeth."

The headmaster clapped. Everyone else clapped, too. Whereupon the boy, in an even louder voice than before, went on again, "And then . . . uh . . ."

The children stopped clapping and listened with bated breath, leaning forward even more.

Finally, the boy said, triumphantly, "And then . . . uh . . . I came to school."

One of the older boys leaned forward so far he lost his balance and hit his face on his lunchbox. But everyone was terribly pleased that the boy had found something to talk about.

The headmaster clapped vigorously, and Totto-chan and the others did, too. Even "And then . . . uh . . . ," who was still standing in their midst, clapped. The Assembly Hall was filled with the sound of clapping.

Even when he was a grown man that boy probably never forgot the sound of that applause.

運動会

トモエの運動会は「十一月三日」と決まっていた。それは、校長先生が、いろんな所に問い合わせた結果、秋で、雨の降ることが最も少ないのが、この十一月三日とわかったので、そう決めて以来、毎年、この日にやることになっていた。前の日から、すっかり校庭にいろんな準備や飾(かざ)りつけをして楽しみにしてる子供たちの運動会に、出来る限り雨が降らないでほしいと願う校長先生の、お天気データ集めが成功したのか、その気持ちが、空の雲や、お陽(ひ)さまに通じたのか、本当に不思議なくらい、この日は雨が降らなかった。

ところで、トモエ学園には随分いろんなことが、ふつうの学校と違っていたけど、運動会は、とりわけユニークなものだった。ふつうの小学校と同じものは、綱引(つなひ)きと、二人三脚(きゃく)くらいのもので、あとは全部、校長先生の考えた競技だった。それも、特別な道具を使うとか、おおげさなものは、なにひとつ無く、すべて、学校にあるおなじみのもので、まにあった。

例えば、「鯉(こい)のぼり競走」というのは、出発点から、ヨーイドン！で、少し走って、校庭のまん中に置いてある、というか、寝ている、大きい布の鯉のぼりの、口から入って、しっぽから出て、また出発点まで帰って来る、というのだった。鯉は、青い色が二匹(ひき)と赤いのが一匹で、合計三匹いたから、三人が同時にヨーイドン！で出発した。でも、これは、やさしいようで、案外むずかしかった。というのは、中に入ると、まっ暗で、胴体(どうたい)が長いから、しばらくゴソゴソやってるうちに、どっちから入ったのかわからなくなって、トットちゃんみたいに、何度も、鯉の口から顔を出して外を見ては、また、いそいで中に、もぐっていく、という風になってしまうからだった。これは、見ている子供たちにとっても、面白かった。というのは、中で誰かがゴソゴソ行ったり来たりしていると、まるで、鯉が生きてるように見えたから。

Sports Day

Tomoe's Sports Day was held every year on the third of November. The headmaster had decided on that day after a lot of research, in which he found out that the third of November was the autumn day on which it had rained the fewest times. Perhaps it was due to his skill in collecting weather data, or perhaps it was just that the sun and clouds heeded his desire—that no rain should mar the Sports Day so anticipated by the children, who had decorated the school grounds the day before and made all sorts of preparations. Whatever it was, it was almost uncanny the way it never rained on that day.

As all kinds of things were done differently at Tomoe, its Sports Day, too, was unique. The only sports events that were the same as at other elementary schools were the Tug of War and the Three-Legged Race. All the rest had been invented by the headmaster. Requiring no special or elaborate equipment, they made use of familiar everyday school things.

For instance, there was the Carp Race. Large tubular cloth streamers, shaped and painted like carp—the kind that are flown from poles in May for the Boys' Day Festival—were laid in the middle of the school grounds. At the signal, the children had to start running toward the carp streamers and crawl through them from the mouth end to the tail end and then run back to the starting point. There were only three carp—one red and two blue—so three children raced

それからまた、「お母さん探し競走」というのもあった。これは、ヨーイドン！　で、少し走って、横に長く置いて立ててある、木の梯子の、段と段の間を通り抜け、そのむこうにある籠の中の封筒から、紙をとり出し、例えばそれに、

「サッコちゃんのお母さん」

と書いてあったら、見物人の中に行って、サッコちゃんのお母さんを探し、手をつないでゴールインするのだった。これは、横にしてある梯子の四角い穴をくぐるのだから、よほど猫みたいに、うまくやらないと、お尻とかがひっかかった。それから、

「サッコちゃんのお母さん」

だったら知ってても、

「奥先生のお姉さん」とか、「津江先生のお母さん」とか、「国則先生の息子さん」になると、逢ったことがないから、見物人のところに行って、

at a time. The race looked easy but was quite difficult. It was dark inside, and the carp were long, so while you were rustling about you could easily lose your sense of direction. Some children, including Totto-chan, kept coming out of the mouth, only to realize their mistake and hurriedly burrow inside again. It was terribly funny to watch because the children crawling backward and forward inside made the carp wriggle as if they were alive.

There was another event called Find-A-Mother Race. At the signal the children had to run toward a wooden ladder propped up on its side, crawl through it between the rungs, take an envelope from a basket, open it, and if the paper inside said, for instance,

「奥先生のお姉さん！」
　と、大きい声で呼ばなきゃならなかったから、少し勇気も必要だった。だから、偶然、自分のお母さんにあたった子は、大よろこびで、
「お母さん！　お母さん！　早く！」
　と、飛び上がりながら叫ぶのだった。そして、この競技は、子供もだけど、見物人も、しっかりしてることが必要だった。子供が次々に走って来て、誰かのお母さんの名前をいうから、呼ばれたお母さんは、ぼんやりしてないで、すぐ、すわっているベンチや、ゴザのところから立ち上がって、他のすわってるお父さんやお母さんたちの間を、「恐れ入ります」なんていいながら、しかも、急いで、すり抜けて、誰かの子供と手をつないで走らなくちゃいけなかったし。だから、お父さんたちも、子供が走って来て、大人の前に止まると、一斉に息を止めて、誰の名前をいうか、その子供に注目した。そんなわけで、大人たちも、雑談したり、なにか喰べてる暇はなく、いつも子供たちと、一緒にやってる気分だった。
　綱引きは、校長先生を始め、全部の先生も二組に別れて、子供たちの中に混じって、
「オー・エス！　オー・エス!!」
　と引っぱった。綱のまん中の、ハンカチのしばってある所に、いつも注意して、
「どっちの組が勝ち！」
　というのは、泰明ちゃんとか、体が不自由で、引っぱることの出来ない子供たちの役目だった。
　そして、最後の全校リレーが、また、トモエらしいのだった。なにしろ、リレーといっても、長く走るところは、あまりなく、勝負どころは、学校の中央にあたる、つまり門にむいて、お扇子型に広がっている、講堂に上がるコンクリートの階段を、かけのぼ

"Sakko-chan's mother," they would have to find her in the crowd of spectators, take her hand, and return together to the finishing line. One had to ease oneself through the ladder with catlike grace or one's bottom could get stuck. Besides that, a child might know well enough who Sakko-chan's mother was, but if the paper read "Miss Oku's sister," or "Mr. Tsue's mother," or "Mrs. Kuninori's son," whom one had never met, one had to go to the spectators' section and call in a loud voice, "Miss Oku's sister!" It took courage. Children who were lucky and picked their own mothers would jump up and down shouting, "Mother! Mother! Hurry!" The spectators, too, had to be alert for this event. There was no telling when their names might be called, and they would have to be ready to get up from the bench or from the mat where they were sitting, excuse themselves, and wend their way out as fast as they could to where someone's child was waiting, take his or her hand, and go running off. So when a child arrived and stopped in front of the grown-ups, even the fathers held their breath, wondering who was going to be called. There was little time for idle chit-chat or nibbling food. The grown-ups had to take part in events almost as much as the children.

The headmaster and other teachers joined the children in the two teams for the Tug of War, pulling and shouting, "Heave-ho, heave-ho!" while handicapped children, like Yasuaki-chan, who couldn't pull, had the task of keeping their eyes on the handkerchief tied to

って、かけおりて来る、という、他には類のないリレーコースだった。ところが、一見、たわいなく見えるのに、この階段の一段一段の高さが、ふつうの階段より、ずーっと低く、傾斜がゆるく、しかも、このリレーのときは、何段も一足とびにやってはいけなくて、丁寧に、一段一段登って一段一段降りて来る、というのだから、足の長い子や、背の高い子には、むしろ、むずかしかった。でも、これは、子供たちにとって、毎日、お弁当の時間にかけ上がる階段が、「運動会用」となると、また別のもののように思えて面白く、新鮮で、みんなキャアキャアいって、上がったり、降りたりした。それは遠くから見ていると、美しく、万華鏡のようにさえ、見えた。階段は、てっぺんまで入れて、八段あった。

　さてトットちゃんたち一年生にとって、初めての運動会は、校長先生の希望どおり、晴天で始まった。みんなで、前の日から、折紙で作った、くさりとか、金色の星とか、いっぱい飾ったからとってもお祭りみたいだったし、レコードの音楽も気持ちがウキウキするようなマーチだった。

　トットちゃんは、白いブラウスに、紺のショートパンツ、という、いでたちだった。本当は、絶対に、ひだのたくさんはいった、ブルーマーがよかったんだけど……。トットちゃんは、ブルーマーに憧れていた。それは、この前、トットちゃんたちの授業が終わったあと、校長先生が幼稚園の保母さんたちに、校庭でリトミックの講習というのをしてるとき、数人の女の人が、ブルーマーをはいていて、それがトットちゃんの目をひいたのだった。なぜ、ブルーマーがよかったかというと、そのブルーマーをはいたお姉さんが、足を、「トン！」と地面につけると、ブルーマーから出ている腿が、〝プルルン〟と揺れて、それがなんとも、大人っぽくてトットちゃんは、

（いいなあ）

　と、憧れたのだった。だからトットちゃんは、走って家に帰る

the center of the rope to see who was winning.

The final Relay Race involving the whole school was also different at Tomoe. No one had to run very far. All one had to do was run up and down the semicircular flight of concrete steps leading to the Assembly Hall. At first glance it looked absurdly easy, but the steps were unusually shallow and close together, and as no one was allowed to take more than one step at a time, it was quite difficult if you were tall or had large feet. The familiar steps, bounded up each day at lunchtime, took on a fresh, fun aspect on Sports Day, and the children hurried up and down them shrieking gaily. To anyone watching from afar, the scene would have looked like a beautiful kaleidoscope. Counting the top one there were eight steps in all.

The first Sports Day for Totto-chan and her classmates was a fine day just as the headmaster had hoped. The decorations of paper chains and gold stars made by the children the day before and the phonograph records of rousing marches made it seem like a festival.

Totto-chan wore navy blue shorts and a white blouse, although she would have preferred to wear athletic bloomers with lots of pleats. She longed to wear them. One day after school the headmaster had been giving a class in eurythmics to some kindergarten teachers, and Totto-chan was very taken with the bloomers some of the women were wearing. What she liked about them was that when the women stamped their feet on the ground, their lower thighs showing

と、自分のショートパンツを引っぱり出し、「トン！」とやってみた。でも、まだ一年生の女の子の、やせた腿では、〝プルルン〟にならなかった。何度もやってみた結果、トットちゃんは、こう考えた。

「あのお姉さんのはいていたのなら〝プルルン〟になる！」

ママにお姉さんのはいてたのを説明したら、それが〝ブルーマー〟というものだとわかった。だからトットちゃんは、絶対に運動会には、「ブルーマー」とママに頼んでいたんだけど、小さいサイズが手に入らないということで、残念ながら、〝プルルン〟なしの、ショートパンツ、というのが、今日のトットちゃんの、いでたち、というわけだった。

さて、運動会が始まって、驚くことが起こった。それは、どの競技も（たいがい全校生徒が一緒にやるのだけれど）、学校で、一番、手足が短く背の小さい、高橋君が一等になっちゃうことだった。それは本当に信じられないことだった。みんなが、モゾモゾしてる鯉のぼりを、高橋君は、ササーッ！　と通り抜けてしまったし、梯子に、みんなが頭をつっこんでる頃、すでに梯子をくぐった高橋君は、さっさと何メートルも先を走っていた。そして講堂の階段のぼりのリレーに到（いた）っては、みんながブキッチョに、一段一段やってる時、高橋君の短い足は、まるでピストンのように一気にのぼりつめ、映画の早まわしフィルムのように、降りて来た。結局、みんなが、

「高橋君に勝とう!!」

と、誓（ちか）い合い、真剣にやったのにもかかわらず、全部、一等になったのは、高橋君だった。トットちゃんも随分、頑張ったけど、一つも高橋君には勝てなかった。ふつうに走るところでは勝つけれど、その先の、いろんなことで、結局、負けちゃうのだった。高橋君は、自慢そうに、鼻を少しピクピクさせ、うれしさと喜びを、いっぱいに体で表現しながら、一等のごほうびを受けとった。

beneath the bloomers rippled in such a lovely grown-up way. She ran home and got out her shorts and put them on and stamped on the floor. But her thin, childish thighs didn't ripple at all. After trying several times, she came to the conclusion it was because of what those ladies had been wearing. She asked what they were and Mother explained they were athletic bloomers. She told Mother she definitely wanted to wear bloomers on Sports Day, but they couldn't find any in a small size. That was why Totto-chan had to make do with shorts, which didn't produce any ripples, alas.

Something amazing happened on Sports Day. Although generally the whole school took part, Takahashi, who had the shortest arms and legs and was the smallest in the school, came first in everything. It was unbelievable. While the others were still creeping about inside the carp, Takahashi was through it in a flash, and while the others only had their heads through the ladder, he was already out of it and running several yards ahead. As for the Relay Race up the Assembly Hall steps, while the others were clumsily negotiating them a step at a time, Takahashi—his short legs moving like pistons—was up them in one spurt and down again like a speeded-up movie.

"We've got to try and beat Takahashi," they all said.

Determined to beat him, the children did their utmost, but try as they might, Takahashi won every time. Totto-chan tried hard, too, but she never managed to beat Takahashi. They could outrun him on the

どれも一等だから、いくつも、いくつも、受けとった。みんなは、うらやましく、それを見ていた。
「来年は高橋君に勝とう！」
　みんな、心の中でそう思った。（でも、結局、毎年、運動会の花形は、高橋君になるのだけど……）
　ところで、この運動会の、ごほうびというか、賞品が、また校長先生らしいものだった。なにしろ、一等が「大根一本」、二等が「ゴボウ二本」、三等が「ホーレン草一束（ひとたば）」という具合なんだから。だからトットちゃんは、随分（ずいぶん）、大きくなるまで、運動会のごほうびは、「どこでも、野菜」だと思っていたくらいだった。
　その頃、他の学校では、たいがい、ノートや鉛筆や、消しゴムなどだった。でも、他の学校のことを知らなくても、みんな、野菜というのには、少し抵抗があった。というのは、トットちゃんにしても、ゴボウとおねぎをいただいたんだけど、それを持って電車に乗るのはなんだか恥ずかしい気がした。そして、この野菜のごほうびは、三等以下にも、いろんな名目で配られたから、運動会の終わったとき、トモエの生徒、みんなが野菜を持っていた。なんで野菜を持って学校から帰るのが恥ずかしいのか、よくわか

straight stretches, but lost to him over the difficult bits.

Takahashi went up to collect his prizes, looking happy and as proud as Punch. He was first in everything so he collected prize after prize. Everyone watched enviously.

"I'll beat Takahashi next year!" said each child to himself. But every year it was Takahashi who turned out to be the star athlete.

Now the prizes, too, were typical of the headmaster. First Prize might be a giant radish; Second Prize, two burdock roots; Third Prize, a bundle of spinach. Things like that. Until she was much older Totto-chan thought all schools gave vegetables for Sports Day prizes.

In those days, most schools gave notebooks, pencils, and erasers for prizes. The Tomoe children didn't know that, but they weren't happy about the vegetables. Totto-chan, for instance, who got some burdock roots and some onions, was embarrassed about having to carry them on the train. Additional prizes were given for various things, so at the end of Sports Day all the children at Tomoe had some sort of vegetable. Now, why should children be embarrassed about going home from school with vegetables? No one minded being sent to buy vegetables by one's mother, but some apparently felt it would look odd carrying vegetables home from school.

A fat boy who won a cabbage didn't know what to do with it.

"I don't want to be seen carrying this," he said. "I

んなかったけど、「ちょっと、かわってる」といわれるといやだと言った子も、いたようだった。お母さんに頼まれて、家から、おつかい籠なんか持って八百屋さんに行くのなら、恥ずかしくないんだけど。

キャベツがあたったデブの男の子は、持ちにくそうに、あれこれ、かかえかたを研究してたけど、とうとう、

「やーだよ。こんなの持って帰るの恥ずかしいよオー。捨てちゃおうかなあー」

といった。校長先生は、みんながグズグズいってるらしいって聞いたのか、人参だの、大根だのを、ぶら下げてるみんなのところに来て、いった。

「なんだ、いやかい？　今晩、お母さんに、これを料理してもらってごらん？　君たちが自分で手に入れた野菜だ。これで、家の人みんなの、おかずが出来るんだぞ。いいじゃないか！　きっと、うまいぞ！」

そういわれてみると、たしかにそうだった。トットちゃんにしても、自分の力で、晩御飯のおかずを手に入れたことは、生まれて初めてだった。だから、トットちゃんは、校長先生にいった。

「私のゴボウで、キンピラをママに作ってもらう！　おねぎは、まだわかんないけど……」

そうなると、みんなも口々に、自分の考えた献立を先生にいった。先生は、顔を真っ赤にして笑いながら、うれしそうにいった。

「そうか！　わかってくれたかい？」

校長先生は、この野菜で、晩御飯をたべながら、家族で楽しく、今日の運動会のことを話してくれたらいい、と思ってたかも知れない。そして、特に、自分で手に入れた一等賞で、食卓が溢れた高橋君が、「その、よろこびを覚えてくれるといい」。背がのびない、小さい、という肉体的なコンプレックスを持ってしまう前に、「一等になった自信を、忘れないでほしい」と校長先生は考えて

think I'll throw it away."

The headmaster must have heard about their complaints for he went over to the children with their carrots and radishes and things.

"What's the matter? Don't you want them?" he asked. Then he went on, "Get your mothers to cook them for you for dinner tonight. They're vegetables you earned yourselves. You have provided food for your families by your own efforts. How's that? I'll bet it tastes good!"

Of course, he was right. It was the first time in her life, for instance, that Totto-chan had ever provided anything for dinner.

"I'll get Mother to make spicy burdock!" she told the headmaster. "I haven't decided yet what to ask her to make with the onions."

Whereupon the others all began thinking up menus, too, describing them to the headmaster.

"Good! So now you've got the idea," he said, smiling so happily his cheeks became quite flushed. He was probably thinking how nice it would be if the children and their families ate the vegetables while talking over the Sports Day events.

No doubt he was thinking especially of Takahashi—whose dinner table would be overflowing with First Prizes—and hoping the boy would remember his pride and happiness at winning those First Prizes before developing an inferiority complex about his size and the fact he would never grow. And maybe, who knows,

いたに違いなかった。そして、もしかすると、もしかだけど、校長先生の考えたトモエ風競技は、どれも高橋君が一等になるように、出来ていたのかも、知れなかった……。

しっぽ

今日の午後のことだった。放課後、家に帰ろうと支度をしてるトットちゃんのところに、大栄君が、走って来て、声をひそめて、いった。

「校長先生が、怒ってる」

「どこで?」

と、トットちゃんは聞いた。だって、校長先生が怒るなんて、それまで知らなかったから、とっても、びっくりしたからだった。大栄君は、大いそぎで走って来たのと、おどろいたらしいので、人の良さそうな目を、まんまるにして、それから、少し鼻をふくらませて、いった。

「校長先生の家の台所のところ」

「行こう!」

トットちゃんは、大栄君の手をつかむと、先生の家の台所のほうに向かって走り出した。校長先生の家は、講堂の横から続いていて、お台所は、校庭の裏口に近いところにあった。いつかトットちゃんが、トイレの汲み取り口に飛び込んだとき、すっかり、綺麗に洗っていただいたのも、この、お台所から入った、お風呂場のところだったし、お弁当のときの「海のもの」と「山のもの」の、おかずが出来るのも、この、お台所だった。

そーっと、二人が足をしのばせて、近づくと、閉まってる戸の中から、本当に、校長先生の怒ってるらしい声がした。その声は、いった。

the headmaster had thought up those singularly Tomoe-type events just so Takahashi would come first in them.

Tails

One afternoon, when school was over and Totto-chan was preparing to go home, Oe came running to her and whispered, "The headmaster's mad at somebody."

"Where?" asked Totto-chan.

She had never heard of the headmaster getting angry and was amazed. Oe was obviously amazed, too, the way he had come running in such a hurry to tell her.

"They're in the kitchen," said Oe, his good-natured eyes opened wide and his nostrils a little dilated.

"Come on!"

Totto-chan took Oe's hand and they both raced toward the headmaster's house. It adjoined the Assembly Hall, and the kitchen was right by the back entrance to the school grounds. The time Totto-chan fell into the cesspool she was taken through the kitchen to the bathroom to be scrubbed clean. And it was in the headmaster's kitchen that "something from the ocean and something from the hills" were made to be doled out at lunchtime.

As the two children tiptoed toward the kitchen, they heard the angry voice of the headmaster through the closed door.

「どうして、あなたは、そんなに、気軽に、高橋君に、『しっぽがある』なんて、いったんですか！」

その怒ってる声に、トットちゃんたちの受け持ちの女の先生の、答えるのが聞こえた。

「そんな深い意味じゃなく、私は、高橋君が目に入って、可愛いいと思ったので、いっただけなんです」

「それが、どんなに深い意味があるか、あなたには、わかってもらえないんですか。僕が、どんなに、高橋君に対しても、気を配っているか、あなたに、どうしたら、わかってもらえるんだろうか！」

トットちゃんは、今日の朝の授業の時のことを思い出した。今朝、この受け持ちの先生は、

「昔、人間には、しっぽが、あった」

という話をしてくれたのだった。これは、とても、楽しい話で、みんな、気に入った。大人の言葉でいえば、進化論の初歩の話、という事になるのだろうけど、とにかく、とても珍しい事で、特に、先生が、

「だから、今でも、みんなに、ビテイコツ、というのが、残っているんです」

といったときは、トットちゃんを始めとしてみんな、お互いに、どれが、ビテイコツか、で、教室は、大さわぎになった。そして、その話の最後のとき、その先生が、冗談に、

「まだ、しっぽの残ってる人も、いるかな？　高橋君は、あるんじゃないの？」

といったのだった。高橋君は、いそいで立ち上がると、小さい手を振って、真剣に、

「ありません」

といった。そのときのことを、校長先生が怒っているのだ、と、トットちゃんには、わかった。

"What made you say so thoughtlessly to Takahashi that he had a tail?"

It was their homeroom teacher who was being reprimanded.

"I didn't mean it seriously," they heard her reply. "I just happened to notice him at that moment, and he looked so cute."

"But can't you see the seriousness of what you said? What can I do to make you understand the care I take with regard to Takahashi?"

Totto-chan remembered what happened in class that morning. The homeroom teacher had been telling them about human beings originally having tails. The children had thought it great fun. Grown-ups would have probably called her talk an introduction to the theory of evolution. It appealed to the children greatly. And when the teacher told them everybody had the vestige of a tail called the coccyx, each child started wondering where his was, and soon the classroom was in an uproar. Finally the teacher had said, jokingly, "Maybe somebody here still has a tail! What about you, Takahashi?"

Takahashi had quickly stood up, shaking his head emphatically, and said in deadly earnest, "I haven't got one."

Totto-chan realized that was what the headmaster was talking about. His voice had now become more sad than angry.

"Did it occur to you to think how Takahashi might

校長先生の声は、怒ってる、というより、悲しそうな声に変わっていた。

「あなたは、高橋君が、あなたに、しっぽがある、といわれて、どんな気がするだろうか、と考えてみたんですか?」

女の先生の、返事は聞こえなかった。トットちゃんには、どうして、校長先生が、こんなに、この、しっぽのことで、怒るのか、わからない、と思った。(もし、私が、先生から、しっぽがあるの?と聞かれたら、うれしくなっちゃうのにな)

確かに、そうだった。トットちゃんは、体には、なんの障害もなかった。だから、「しっぽがあるか?」と聞かれても、平気だった。でも、高橋君は、背が、のびない体質で、自分でも、もう、それを知っていた。だから、校長先生は、運動会でも、高橋君が勝つような競技を考えたり、体の障害という羞恥心(しゅうちしん)を無くすために、みんな海水着なしで、プールに一緒に入るように考えたり、とにかく、高橋君や、泰明(やすあき)ちゃんや、その他、肉体的な障害のある子から、そのコンプレックスや、「他の子より、劣ってる」という考えを取るために、出来るだけの事を、していたし、事実、みんな、コンプレックスを持っていなかった。それなのに、いくら、可愛いく見えたからといって、よりによって高橋君に、「しっぽがあるんじゃない?」というような不用意な発言は、校長先生には、考えられないことだった。これは偶然、朝の授業を、校長先生が、後ろで参観して、わかったことだった。

女の先生が、涙声で、こういうのが、トットちゃんに聞こえた。

「本当に、私が、間違ってました。高橋君に、なんて、あやまったら、いいんでしょう……」

校長先生はだまっていた。そのとき、トットちゃんは、ガラス戸で見えない校長先生に(逢いたい)と、思った。わけは、わからないけど、校長先生は、本当に、私たちの、友達だと、いつもより、もっと強く感じたからだった。大栄君も同じ考えだったに、

feel if he was asked if he had a tail?"

The children couldn't hear the teacher's reply. Totto-chan didn't understand why the headmaster was so angry about the tail. She would have loved being asked by the headmaster if she had a tail.

Of course, she had nothing wrong with her, so she wouldn't have minded such a question. But Takahashi had stopped growing, and he knew it. That was why the headmaster had thought up events for Sports Day in which Takahashi would do well. He had them swim in the pool without swimsuits so children like Takahashi would lose their self-consciousness. He did all he could to help children with physical handicaps, like Takahashi and Yasuaki-chan, lose any complexes they might have and the feeling they were inferior to other children. So they were all, in fact, quite complex-free. Still, it was beyond the headmaster's comprehension how anyone could be so thoughtless as to ask Takahashi, just because he looked cute, whether he had a tail.

The headmaster happened to be visiting that class, standing in the back of the classroom, when she said it.

Totto-chan could hear the homeroom teacher crying. "It was terribly wrong of me," she sobbed. "What can I do to apologize to Takahashi?"

The headmaster said nothing. Totto-chan couldn't see him through the glass door, but she wanted so much to be with him. She didn't know what it was all about, but somehow she felt more than ever that he was their

違いなかった。
　校長先生が、他の先生のいる職員室じゃなく、台所で、受け持ちの先生に怒っていた事を、トットちゃんは、忘れなかった。（そこに、小林先生の、本当の教育者としての姿があったから……）という事は、トットちゃんには、わかっていなかったんだけど、なぜか、いつまでも、心に残る、先生の声だった。
　春が……トットちゃんにとって、トモエでの、二度目の春が、もう、本当に、近くまで、来ていた。

畠の先生

「いいかい？　今日の先生だよ。なんでも教えてくださるからね」
　校長先生は、こういって、一人の男の先生を、みんなに紹介した。トットちゃんは、つくづくとその先生を観察した。なにしろ、その先生の恰好は、かわっていた。上着は縞のハンテンで、胸からは、メリヤスのシャツが、のぞいていて、ネクタイのかわりに、首には手拭いが、ぶら下がっていた。そして、ズボンは、紺の木綿のパッチ風の細いのだし、靴じゃなくて、地下足袋だった。おまけに、頭には、少し破れた麦わら帽子をかぶっていた。
　いまトットちゃんたちが、どこにいるか、といえば、九品仏の池のほとりだった。
　しばらく、その先生をジロジロ見ていたトットちゃんは、その先生に、見覚えがあることを発見した。
（えーと、えーと……）
　顔色は陽焼けして、真黒だった。そして、その顔に、しわはあるけど、やさしそうだった。腰にむすんであるベルトみたいな黒

friend. Oe must have felt that way, too.

Totto-chan never forgot how the headmaster had reprimanded their homeroom teacher in his kitchen and not in the faculty room, where the other teachers were. It showed he was an educator in the very best sense of the word, although Totto-chan did not realize that at the time. The sound of his voice and his words remained in her heart forever.

It was almost spring, Totto-chan's second spring at Tomoe, and the beginning of a new school year.

The Farming Teacher

"This is your teacher today. He's going to show you all sorts of things." With that the headmaster introduced a new teacher. Totto-chan took a good look at him. In the first place, he wasn't dressed like a teacher at all. He wore a short striped cotton work jacket over his undershirt, and instead of a necktie, he had a towel hanging around his neck. As for his trousers, they were of indigo-dyed cotton with narrow legs, and were full of patches. Instead of shoes, he wore workmen's thick two-toed rubber-soled socks, while on his head was a rather dilapidated straw hat.

The children were all assembled by the pond at Kuhonbutsu Temple.

As she stared at the teacher, Totto-chan thought she had seen him before. "Where?" she wondered. His

い紐にぶら下げてあるキセルも、何か初めて見る感じじゃなかった……。
（わかった！）
　トットちゃんは、思い出した。
「ねえ、先生って、いつも、あそこの川のそばの畠にいる、お百姓さんじゃないの?」
　トットちゃんは、すっかり、うれしくなって、いった。すると、地下足袋の、その先生は、白い歯を見せ、顔中を、しわくしゃにして、笑っていった。
「そうだよ。みんな、九品仏のお寺に散歩に行くとき、家のそばを通るじゃねえの?　いま、菜の花が咲いてる、あすこの畠。あれが家のだから」
「わあ！　おじさんが、今日は先生なのか!?」
　トットちゃんたちは、すっかり興奮した。人の良さそうな、おじさんは手を振っていった。
「いやいや、私は先生なんかじゃなくて、百姓です。今日は、校長先生に頼まれたんでね」
　校長先生は、お百姓さん先生の隣りに並ぶと、いった。

kindly face was sunburnt and full of wrinkles. Even the slender pipe dangling from a black cord around his waist that served as a belt looked familiar. She suddenly remembered!

"Aren't you the farmer who works in the field by the stream?" she asked him, delighted.

"That's right," said the "teacher," with a toothy smile, wrinkling up his face. "You pass my place ev'ry time you go fer yer walks to Kuhonbutsu! That's my field. That one over there full o' mustard blossoms."

"Wow! So you're going to be our teacher today," cried the children excitedly.

"Naw!" said the good-natured looking man, waving his hand in front of his face. "I ain't no teacher! I'm just a farmer. Your headmaster just asked me to do it, that's all."

"Oh yes, he is. He's your farming teacher," said the headmaster, standing beside him. "He very kindly

「いや、これから、畠の作りかたを、あなたに教えてもらうのだから。畠の事については、あなたは先生です。パンの作りかたを習うときは、パン屋さんに先生になってもらうのと同じです。さあ、どんどん、子供たちに指図して、始めてください」

　きっと、ふつうの小学校では、生徒に、なにかを教える人には、「先生の資格」とか、いろいろ規則があるだろうけど、小林先生は、かまわなかった。子供たちに、「本物」を見せる事が必要なのだし、それが、大切なことだ、と先生は考えていた。

「じゃ、始めっかな?」

　畠の先生はいった。みんなの、立っている場所は、九品仏の池のまわりでも、特に静かなところにあり、木が池に影を落としているという、感じのいいところだった。校長先生は、すでに、スコップとか、くわ、とか、その他、畠に必要な道具をしまっておく物置にするために、ふつうの一台の半分の電車を、運んで来てあった。半分の電車は、小さい畠になる予定の土地の、丁度まん中に、こぢんまりと、静かに置いてあった。

　電車の中から、スコップとか、くわを運び出すように生徒にい

agreed to teach you how to plant a field. It's like having a baker teach you how to make bread. Now then," he said to the farmer, "tell the children what to do, and let's get started."

At an ordinary elementary school, anyone who taught the children anything would probably have to have teaching qualifications, but Mr. Kobayashi didn't worry about things like that. He thought it important for children to learn by actually seeing things done.

"Let's begin then," said the farming teacher.

The place where they were assembled was beside the Kuhonbutsu pond and it was a particularly quiet section—a pleasant place, where the pond was shaded by trees. The headmaster had already had part of a railroad car put there for storing the children's farming implements, such as spades and hoes. The half-car had a peaceful look, neatly placed as it was right in the middle of the plot they were going to cultivate.

The farming teacher told the children to get spades and hoes from the car and started them on weeding. He told them all about weeds: how hardy they were; how some grew faster than crops and hid the sun from them; how weeds were good hiding places for bad insects; and how weeds could be a nuisance by taking all the nourishment from the soil. He taught them one thing after another. And while he talked, his hands never stopped pulling out weeds. The children did the same. Then the teacher showed them how to hoe; how to make furrows; how to sow *daikon* and other seeds; how to spread

うと、畠の先生は、まず草むしりから始めた。先生は雑草について話した。「雑草が、どんなに丈夫なものか」という事や、「雑草によっては、作物より、のびるのが、早いのがあって、おかげで作物に陽があたらなくなってしまう」とか、「雑草は、悪い虫の、いい、かくれ場所だ」とか、「雑草は、土から栄養をとってしまうから困るのだ」とか、もう次から次と、教えてくれた。しかも、話しながら、手は休むことなく雑草を、ひきぬいた。みんなも同じようにやった。それから先生は、くわで耕すこと、うねを作ること、大根などの、種のまきかた、肥料のやりかたなど、畠に必要なことを、実際に、やって見せてくれながら説明した。途中で、小さい蛇が頭を出して、上級生のタアーちゃんが、もう少しで手を嚙まれそうになったりもしたけど、畠の先生は、

「このあたりの蛇は毒もないし、こっちが、何かしなければ、あっちから嚙みついてくる事もないのだから」

と安心させてくれたりもした。とにかく、畠の先生は、畠の作りかただけじゃなく、虫のこと、鳥のこと、蝶々のこと、天気のこと、もう、いろんなことを、面白く話してくれた。節くれだった先生の丈夫な手が、そういう話は、どれもこれも、畠の先生が体験し、自分で発見したのだ、という事を証明しているようだった。みんなは、汗びっしょりで、先生に手をとってもらって、遂に畠は完成した。どこから見ても……少しグニャグニャのうねはあったけど……完璧な畠だった。

この日以来、トモエの生徒は、その、おじさんに逢うと、

「畠の先生！」

と、遠くからでも、尊敬をこめて、叫んだ。畠の先生は、自分の畠にあまった肥料を、学校の畠に、少しまいといてくれる事もあった。みんなの畠は、順調に成長した。毎日、誰かが、見回りに出かけては、校長先生やみんなに、畠の様子を報告した。「自分のまいた種から、芽がでる」という事が、どんなに不思議であり、

fertilizer; and everything else you had to do to grow things in a field, explaining as he demonstrated.

A little snake put its head out and very nearly bit the hand of Ta-chan, one of the older boys, but the farming teacher reassured him, "The snakes here ain't poisonous, and they won't hurt you if you don't hurt them."

Besides teaching the children how to plant a field, the farming teacher told them interesting things about insects, birds, and butterflies, about the weather, and about all sorts of other things. His strong gnarled hands seemed to attest that everything he told the children, he had found out himself through experience.

The children were dripping with perspiration when they had finally finished planting the field with the teacher's help. Except for a few furrows that were a bit uneven, it was an impeccable field, whichever way you looked at it.

From that day onward, the children held that farmer in high esteem, and whenever they saw him, even at a distance, they would cry, "There's our farming teacher!" Whenever he had any fertilizer left he would bring it over and spread it on the children's field, and their crops grew well. Every day someone would visit the field and report to the headmaster and the other children on how it was doing. The children learned to know the wonder and the joy of seeing the seeds they had planted themselves sprout. And whenever two or three of them were gathered together, talk would turn

驚きであり、そして、よろこびであるかを、子供たちは、知った。みんな、何人か集まると、畠の成長について、話しあった。
　世界の、いろいろなところで、少しずつ恐ろしい事が始まっていた。でも、この小さな畠について真剣に話しあってる子供たちは、ありがたいことに、まだ、平和そのものの中に、いたのだった。

「本当は、いい子なんだよ」

　校長先生は、トットちゃんを見かけると、いつも、いった。
「君は、本当は、いい子なんだよ！」
　そのたびにトットちゃんは、ニッコリして、とびはねながら答えた。
「そうです、私は、いい子です！」
　そして、自分でもいい子だと思っていた。
　たしかにトットちゃんは、いい子のところもたくさんあった。みんなに親切だったし、特に肉体的なハンディキャップがあるために、よその学校の子にいじめられたりする友達のためには、他の学校の生徒に、むしゃぶりついていって、自分が泣かされても、そういう子の力になろうとしたし、怪我をした動物を見つけると、必死で看病もした。でも同時に、珍しいものや、興味のある事を見つけたときには、その自分の好奇心を満たすために、先生たちが、びっくりするような事件を、いくつも起こしていた。
　例えば、朝礼で行進をするときに、頭の毛を二本、おさげにして、それぞれの尻っぽを、後ろから、両方の、わきの下から出し、腕で、はさんで、見せびらかして歩いてみたり。お掃除の当番のとき、電車の教室の床のフタを上げて……それはモーターの点検用の上げブタだったんだけど、それを目ざとく見つけて持ち上げ

to the progress of their field.

Terrible things were beginning to happen in various parts of the world. But as the children discussed their tiny field, they were still enfolded in the very heart of peace.

"You're Really a Good Girl"

"You're really a good girl, you know."

That's what the headmaster used to say every time he saw Totto-chan. And every time he said it, Totto-chan would smile, give a little skip, and say, "Yes, I am a good girl." And she believed it.

Totto-chan was, indeed, a good girl in many ways. She was kind to everyone—particularly her physically handicapped friends. She would defend them, and, if children from other schools said cruel things, she would fight the tormentors, even if it ended with her crying. She would do everything to care for any injured animals she found. But at the same time her teachers were continually astonished at the amount of trouble she always got into as she tried to satisfy her curiosity whenever she discovered anything unusual.

She would do things like making her pigtails stick out behind under each arm while marching to morning assembly. Once, when it was her turn to sweep the classroom, she opened a trapdoor her sharp eyes had

て……、ゴミを捨てて、いざ閉めようとしたら、もう閉まらないので、大さわぎになったり。また、ある日は、誰かから、牛肉は大きな肉の固まりが、鉤からぶら下がってると聞くと、朝から一番たかい鉄棒に片手だけで、ぶら下がって、いつまでも、そのままでいる。女の先生が、「どうしたの?」と聞くと、「私は今日、牛肉！」と叫び、とたんに落ちて、「ウッ！」といったまま、一日中、声が出なくなったり。お昼休み、学校の裏をブラブラ歩いていて、道に新聞紙がひろげて置いてあるので、とてもうれしくなって、遠くから、はずみをつけて、凄い、いきおいで走って来て、その新聞紙に、とび乗ったら、それは清掃の人が、トイレの汲み取り口をどかして、におうといけないので、のせてあっただけだから、そのまま、汲み取り口に、ズボ！っと、胸まで、つかってしまったり……。そんな風に、自分自身が、痛い目にあう事も、しょっちゅうだった。でも校長先生は、そういう事件が起きたときに、絶対に、パパやママを呼び出すことはなかった。他の生徒でも同じことだった。いつも、それは、校長先生と、生徒との間で解決した。初めて学校に来た日に、トットちゃんの話を、四時間も聞いてくれたように、校長先生は、事件を起こした、どの生徒の話も、聞いてくれた。その上、いいわけだって、聞いてくれた。そして、本当に、「その子のした事が悪い」とき、そして、「そ

noticed in the floor and put all the sweepings down the hole. It had originally been for inspecting the machinery when it was a real train. She couldn't get the trapdoor closed again, and caused everyone a lot of trouble. And then there was the time someone told her how meat was hung up on hooks, so she went and hung by one arm from the highest exercise bar. She hung there for ages, and when a teacher saw her and asked what she was doing, she shouted, "I'm a piece of meat today!" and just then lost her hold and fell down so hard it knocked all the wind out of her lungs and she couldn't speak all day. And that lunch break when she was sauntering along behind the school, and saw the newspapers spread out on the path, and just for fun took a long running leap and jumped onto them with terrific force, but they had been put there to stop the smell by the man cleaning the cesspool, who had removed the cover, so she fell straight in with a plop right up to her chest.

She was always doing things like that and hurting herself, but the headmaster never sent for Mother and Daddy. It was the same with the other children. Matters were always settled between the headmaster and the child concerned. Just as he had listened to Totto-chan for four hours the day she first arrived at the school, he always listened to what a child had to say about an incident caused. He even listened to their excuses. And if the child had done something really bad and eventually recognized it was wrong, the head-

の子が自分で悪い」と納得したとき、
「あやまりなさい」
　といった。でも、おそらく、トットちゃんに関しては、苦情や心配の声が、生徒の父兄や、他の先生たちから、校長先生の耳にとどいているに違いなかった。だから校長先生は、トットちゃんに、機会あるごとに、
「君は、本当は、いい子なんだよ」
　といった。その言葉を、もし、よく気をつけて大人が聞けば、この「本当は」に、とても大きな意味があるのに、気がついたはずだった。
「いい子じゃないと、君は、人に思われているところが、いろいろあるけど、君の本当の性格は悪くなくて、いいところがあって、校長先生には、それが、よくわかっているんだよ」
　校長の小林先生は、こう、トットちゃんに伝えたかったに違いなかった。残念だけど、トットちゃんが、この本当の意味がわかったのは、何十年も、経（た）ってからのことだった。でも、本当の意味は、わからなくても、トットちゃんの心の中に、「私は、いい子なんだ」という自信をつけてくれたのは、事実だった。だって、いつも、なにかをやるとき、この先生の言葉を思い出していたんだから。ただ、やったあとで、「あれ?」と思うことは、ときどき、あったんだけど。
　そして、トットちゃんの一生を決定したのかも知れないくらい、大切な、この言葉を、トットちゃんが、トモエにいる間じゅう、小林先生は、いい続けてくれたのだった。
「トットちゃん、君は、本当は、いい子なんだよ」って。

master would say, "Now apologize."

In Totto-chan's case, complaints and fears voiced by children's parents and other teachers undoubtedly reached the ears of the headmaster. That's why, whenever he had a chance, he would say to Totto-chan, "You're really a good girl, you know." A grown-up, hearing him say it, would have realized the significance of the way he emphasized the word "really."

What the headmaster must have wanted to make Totto-chan understand was something like this: "Some people may think you're not a good girl in many respects, but your real character is not bad. It has a great deal that is good about it, and I am well aware of that." Alas, it was many, many years before Totto-chan realized what he really meant. Still, while she may not have grasped his true meaning at the time, the headmaster certainly instilled, deep in her, a confidence in herself as "a good girl." His words echoed in her heart even when she was engaged in some escapade. And many times she said to herself, "Good heavens!" as she reflected on something she had done.

Mr. Kobayashi kept on repeating, the entire time she was at Tomoe, those important words that probably determined the course of her whole life:

"Totto-chan, you're really a good girl, you know."

お嫁さん

今日、トットちゃんは、悲しかった。

もう、トットちゃんは、三年生になっていて、同級生の泰ちゃんを、とても好きだと思っていた。頭がよくて、物理が出来た。英語を勉強していて、最初に「キツネ」という英語を教えてくれたのも、泰ちゃんだった。

「トットちゃん、キツネは、フォックスだよ」

（フォックスかあ……）

その日、トットちゃんは、一日、〝フォックス〟という響きに、ひたったくらいだった。だから、毎朝、電車の教室に行くと、最初にする事は、泰ちゃんの筆箱の中の鉛筆を、全部ナイフで、きれいに、けずってあげる事だった。自分の鉛筆ときたら、歯でむしりとって、使っているというのに。

ところが、今日、その泰ちゃんが、トットちゃんを呼びとめた。そのとき、トットちゃんは、昼休みなので、ブラブラと講堂の裏の、例のトイレの汲み取り口のあたりを散歩してたんだけど、

「トットちゃん！」

という泰ちゃんの声が、怒ってるみたいなので、びっくりして立ち止まった。泰ちゃんは、一息つくと、いった。

「大きくなって、君がどんなに頼んでも、僕のお嫁さんには、してあげないからね！」

それだけいうと、泰ちゃんは、下をむいたまま、歩いて行ってしまった。トットちゃんは、ポカンとして、その泰ちゃんの頭が……脳味噌が、いっぱいつまっている、自分の尊敬してる頭。仮分数、という仇名の頭が……見えなくなるまで見ていた。

トットちゃんは、ポケットに手をつっこんだまま考えた。思いあたる事は、ないように思えた。仕方なく、トットちゃんは、同級生のミヨちゃんに相談した。ミヨちゃんは、トットちゃんの話を聞くと、大人っぽい口調で、こういった。

His Bride

Totto-chan was very sad.

She was in third grade now and she liked Tai-chan a lot. He was clever and good at physics. He studied English, and it was he who taught her the English word for fox.

"Totto-chan," he had said, "do you know what the English word for *kitsune* is? It's 'fox.' "

"Fox."

Totto-chan had luxuriated in the sound of that word all day long. After that, the first thing she always did when she got to the classroom-in-the-train was to sharpen all the pencils in Tai-chan's pencil box as beautifully as she could with her penknife. She didn't bother about her own, which she just hacked at with her teeth.

In spite of all that, Tai-chan had spoken roughly to her. It happened during lunch break. Totto-chan was sauntering along behind the Assembly Hall in the region of that notorious cesspool.

"Totto-chan!"

Tai-chan's voice sounded cross, and she stopped, startled. Pausing for breath, Tai-chan said, "When I grow up, I'm not going to marry you, no matter how much you ask me to." So saying, he walked off, his eyes on the ground.

Totto-chan stood dazed, watching until he and his large head disappeared from view. That head full of brains that she admired so much. That head that looked so much bigger than his body the children used

「そりゃ、そうよ。だって、トットちゃん、今日、お相撲(すもう)の時間に、泰ちゃんのこと、投げとばしたじゃないの。泰ちゃんは、頭が重いから、ずーっと、土俵の外に、すっとんだんだもの。そりゃ、怒るわよ」

トットちゃんは、心の底から後悔(こうかい)した。(そうだった)、毎日、鉛筆をけずってあげるくらい好きな人を、なんで、お相撲の時間に、すっかり忘れて、投げとばしちゃったんだろう……。でも、もう遅かった。トットちゃんが、泰ちゃんのお嫁さんになれない事は、決まってしまった。

(でも、明日から、やっぱり、鉛筆は、けずってあげよう)

だって、好きなんだもの。

お見舞い

トットちゃんは、今日、生まれて初めて、戦争で怪我(けが)をした兵隊さんのたくさんいる病院に行った。一緒に三十人くらいの小学生が行ったけど、みんな、いろいろの学校から集まって来た知らない子たちだった。いつの頃からか、国の命令によるもののようだったけど、一つの小学校から、二人とか三人、トモエのように人数の少ない学校は一人とか、そんな風に、お見舞いに行く子が決まると、三十人くらいのグループにまとめて、どこかの学校の先生が引率して、兵隊さんの入っている病院に行く、というようなことが、少しずつ始まっていた。そして、今日は、トモエから

to call him "The Improper Fraction."

Totto-chan put her hands in her pockets and thought. She could not remember doing anything to annoy him. In desperation she talked it over with her classmate Miyo-chan. After listening to Totto-chan, Miyo-chan said, maturely, "Why, of course! It's because you threw Tai-chan out of the ring today at sumo wrestling. It's not surprising he flew out of the ring the way he did because his head's so heavy. But he's still bound to be mad at you."

Totto-chan regretted it with all her heart. Yes, that was it. What on earth made her beat the boy she liked so much she sharpened his pencils every day? But it was too late. She could never be his bride now.

"I'm going to go on sharpening his pencils all the same," Totto-chan decided. "After all, I love him."

Visiting the Wounded

For the first time in her life Totto-chan visited a hospital for wounded soldiers. She went with about thirty elementary school children from various schools, children she didn't know. It was part of a scheme recently organized nationally. Each school would normally send two or three children, but small schools like Tomoe only sent one, and the group would be in the charge of a teacher from one of the schools. Totto-chan was representing Tomoe.

は、トットちゃんだった。引率の先生は、目がねをかけて、やせた、どこかの学校の女の先生だった。その先生に連れられて、病院の部屋に入ると、白い寝巻きを着た兵隊さんが、十五人くらい、ベッドの中にいたり、起き上がったりして、むかえてくれた。怪我してるって、どんなのかと、トットちゃんは心配してたけど、みんながニコニコしたり、手を振ったり、元気なので安心した。でも、頭に包帯してる兵隊さんもいた。女の先生は、部屋の、だいたい、まん中へんに子供を、まとめると、まず、兵隊さんに、

「お見舞いに参りました」

と、あいさつをした。みんなも、おじぎをした。先生は続けて、

「今日は、五月五日で、端午(たんご)のお節句ですので、『鯉(こい)のぼりの歌』を歌いましょう」

といって、早速、手を指揮者のように、高くあげ、子供たちに、

「さあ、いいですか？　三！　四！」

というと、元気に、手をふりおろした。顔見知りじゃない子供たちも、みんな、大きな声で、一斉(いっせい)に歌い始めた。

〽いらかの波と、雲の波……

ところが、トットちゃんは、この歌を知らなかった。トモエでは、こういう歌を、教えていなかったから。トットちゃんは、そのとき、優しそうで、ベッドの上に正座してる兵隊さんのベッド

The teacher in charge was a thin woman who wore glasses. She led the children into a ward where there were about fifteen soldiers in white pajamas, some in bed and others walking about. Totto-chan had worried about what wounded soldiers would look like, but they all smiled and waved their hands and seemed cheerful so she was relieved, although some had bandages on their heads.

The teacher assembled the children in the middle of the ward and addressed the soldiers.

"We've come to visit you," she said, and the children all bowed. The teacher went on, "Since today is the fifth of May—Boy's Day—we're going to sing 'Carp Streamers.' "

She raised her arms, like a conductor, said to the children, "Now, ready? Three, four," and began to beat time. The children didn't know each other but they all began singing wholeheartedly:

Over the sea of rooftops,
Over the sea of clouds . . .

Totto-chan didn't know the song. They didn't teach that sort of song at Tomoe. She sat on the edge of the bed of a man with a kind face who was sitting up, and just listened to them singing, feeling rather awkward. When that song was over, the teacher announced very clearly, "Now we shall sing 'The Doll Festival.' " They sang it beautifully. All except Totto-chan.

Come let us light the lanterns,
Light them one by one . . .

のはじに、人なつっこく腰をかけて、「困ったな」と思いながら、みんなの歌を聞いていた。

〽いらかの波と……

が終わると、女の先生は、いった。はっきりと。

「では、今度は、『ひな祭り』です」

トットちゃん以外の、みんなは、きれいに歌った。

〽あかりをつけましょ、ぼんぼりに……

トットちゃんは、だまっているしかなかった。

みんなが歌い終わると、兵隊さんが拍手をした。女の先生は、にっこりすると、「では」といってから、

「みなさん、『お馬の親子』ですよ、元気よく、さあ、三！　四！」

と、指揮を始めた。

これも、トットちゃんの知らない歌だった。みんなが、「お馬の親子」を歌い終わったときだった。トットちゃんの腰かけてるベッドの兵隊さんが、トットちゃんの頭をなでて、いった。

「君は、歌わないんだね」

トットちゃんは、とても申しわけない、と思った。お見舞いに来たのに、一つも歌わないなんて。だから、トットちゃんは、ベッドから離れて立つと、勇気を出して、いった。

「じゃ、あたしの知ってるの、歌います」

女の先生は、命令と違う事が始まったので、

「なんです?」

と聞いたけど、トットちゃんが、もう息を吸いこんで歌おうとしてるので、だまって聞く事にしたらしかった。

トットちゃんは、トモエの代表として、一番、トモエで有名な歌がいい、と思った。

だから、息を吸うと、大きい声で歌い始めた。

〽よく噛めよ、たべものを……

まわりの子供たちから、笑い声が起こった。中には、

There was nothing Totto-chan could do but remain silent.

When they had all finished singing, the men clapped. The teacher smiled and said, "Now then, what about 'The Pony and the Mare'? All together. Three, four," and started beating time again.

Totto-chan didn't know that one either. When the children had finished singing it, the soldier in the bed Totto-chan was sitting on patted her head and said, "You didn't sing."

Totto-chan felt very apologetic. She had come to visit the soldiers and she couldn't even sing them a single song. So she got up, and, standing a little away from the bed, said bravely, "All right. Now I'll sing one I know."

Something was about to happen that wasn't according to plan.

"What are you going to sing?" asked the teacher. But Totto-chan had already taken a deep breath and was starting to sing, so she decided to wait.

Since she was representing Tomoe, Totto-chan thought she had better sing Tomoe's best-known song. After taking that deep breath, she began:

> Chew, chew, chew it well,
> Everything you eat . . .

Some of the children laughed. Others asked their neighbors, "What's the song? What's the song?" The teacher started to beat time, but not knowing quite what to do, was left with arms in midair. Totto-chan

「なんの歌？　なんの歌？」
　と、隣りの子に聞いてる子もいた。女の先生は、指揮のやりようがなくて、手を空中にあげたままだった。トットちゃんは、恥ずかしかったけど、一生懸命に歌った。
　〽噛めよ噛めよ噛めよ噛めよ、たべものを……
　歌い終わると、トットちゃんは、おじぎをした。頭をあげたとき、トットちゃんは、その兵隊さんの目から、涙が、こぼれているのを見て、びっくりした。なにか、悪い事をしたのか、と思ったから。すると、その、パパより少し歳（とし）をとったくらいの兵隊さんは、また、トットちゃんの頭をなでて、
「ありがとう、ありがとう」
　といった。
　頭をなでてくれながら、兵隊さんの涙は止まらないみたいだった。そのとき、女の先生は、気をとり直すような声で、いった。
「じゃ、ここで、みんなの、おみやげの、作文を、読みましょう」
　子供たちは、自分の作文を、ひとりずつ、読み始めた。トットちゃんは、兵隊さんを、見た。兵隊さんは、目と、鼻を赤くしながら、笑った。トットちゃんも、笑った。そして、思った。
（よかった。兵隊さんが笑った）
　兵隊さんの涙が、なんであったのか、それは、その兵隊さんにしか、わからないことだった。もしかすると、それは、故郷（こきょう）に、トットちゃんに似た子を残して来ていたのかも、知れなかった。それとも、トットちゃんが、あまり一生懸命に歌ったので、いじらしく、可愛く思ったのかも知れなかった。そして、もしかすると、戦地での体験で、（もうじき食べものもなくなるのに、〝よく噛（か）めよ〟の歌をうたってる）と、可哀そうに思ったのかも知れなかった。そして兵隊さんには、この子供たちが、これから巻きこまれる、本当の恐ろしいことが、わかっていたのかも、知れなかった。

was embarrassed, but she sang for all she was worth:

Chew it and chew it and chew it and chew it,
Your rice and fish and meat!

When she finished singing, Totto-chan bowed. When she raised her head, she was astonished to see tears streaming down the face of the soldier. She thought she must have done something bad. And then the soldier, who looked a little older than Daddy, patted her head again, and said, "Thank you! Thank you!"

He went on patting her head, and he couldn't stop crying. Then the teacher said brightly, as if to try and cheer him up, "Now I think it's time to read out the compositions we've written for the soldiers."

The children took turns reading their compositions aloud. Totto-chan looked at her soldier. His nose and eyes were red, but he smiled. Totto-chan smiled back. And she thought to herself, "I'm so glad the soldier smiled!"

What had brought tears to that soldier's eyes, only the soldier knew. Maybe he had a little girl like Totto-chan. Or maybe he was simply touched by the sweet way she sang that song as best she could. Or maybe because of his experience at the war front, he knew how near they all were to starvation, and the thought of this little girl singing "Chew it well" when there might soon be nothing left to chew may have filled him with sadness. The soldier may also have realized what terrible events would soon engulf these very children.

作文を読む子供たちの知らないうちに、太平洋戦争は、もう、いつのまにか、始まっていたのだった。

英語の子

今日は、新しい生徒がトモエに来た。小学校の生徒にしては、誰よりも背が高く、全体的にも凄く大きかった。小学生というよりは、

「中学生のお兄さんみたいだ」

と、トットちゃんは思った。着てるものも、みんなと違って、大人のひと、みたいだったし。

校長先生は、朝、校庭で、みんなに、この新しい生徒を、こう紹介した。

「宮崎君だ。アメリカで生まれて、育ったから、日本語は、あまり上手(じょうず)じゃない。だから、ふつうの学校より、トモエのほうが、友達も、すぐ出来るだろうし、ゆっくり勉強できるんじゃないか、という事で、今日から、みんなと一緒だよ。何年生がいいかなあ。どうだい、タアーちゃんたちと一緒の、五年生じゃ」

絵の上手な、五年生のタアーちゃんは、いつものようにお兄さんらしく、いった。

「いいよ」

校長先生は、にっこり笑うと、いった。

「日本語は、うまくない、といったけど、英語は得意だからね、教えてもらうといい。だけど、日本の生活に馴(な)れていないから、いろいろ教えてあげてください。アメリカの生活の話も、聞いてごらん。面白いから。じゃ、いいね」

宮崎君は、自分より、ずーっと、小さい同級生に、おじぎをし

The children, reading their compositions, may not have sensed it then, but the Pacific War was already well underway.

The English-speaking Child

A new pupil arrived at Tomoe. He was tall for an elementary school boy, and broad. Totto-chan thought he looked more like a seventh grader. His clothes were different, too, more like grown-up ones.

That morning in the school grounds the headmaster introduced the new student.

"This is Miyazaki. He was born and brought up in America, so he doesn't speak Japanese very well. That's why he has come to Tomoe, where he will be able to make friends more easily and take his time over his studies. He's one of you now. What grade shall we put him in? What about fifth grade, with Ta-chan and the others?"

"That's fine," said Ta-chan—who was good at drawing—in a big-brotherly voice.

The headmaster smiled and went on, "I said he wasn't very good at Japanese, but he's very good at English. Get him to teach you some. He's not used to life in Japan, though, so you'll help him, won't you? And ask him about life in America. He'll be able to tell you all sorts of interesting things. Well, then, I'll leave him with you."

た。タアーちゃんたちのクラスだけじゃなく、他の子も、みんな、おじぎをしたり、手を振ったりした。

お昼休みに、宮崎君が、校長先生の、家のほうに行くと、みんなも、ゾロゾロついて行った。そしたら、宮崎君は、家にあがるとき、靴をはいたまま、畳(たたみ)にあがろうとしたから、みんなは、

「靴は、ぬぐの!」

と大さわぎで、教えてあげた。宮崎君は、びっくりしたように、靴をぬぐと、

「ゴメンナサイ」

といった。みんなは、口々に、

「畳はぬぐけど、電車の教室と、図書室は、ぬがなくていい」

とか、

「九品仏(くほんぶつ)のお寺の、お庭はいいけど、本堂は、ぬぐの」

とか、教えた。そして、日本人でも、ずーっと外国で生活していると、いろんなことが違うのだと、みんなにも、よくわかって、面白かった。

次の日、宮崎君は、英語の、大きい絵本を、学校に持って来た。お昼休みに、みんなは、宮崎君を、何重(なんじゅう)にも、とりかこんで、その絵本を、のぞきこんだ。そして、おどろいた。第一に、こんな、きれいな絵本を見た事が、なかったからだった。みんなの知ってる絵本は、ふつう、色が、まっ赤、とか、みどり色とか、まっ黄色という風なのに、この絵本の色は、薄い肌色(はだいろ)のようなピンクとか、水色

Miyazaki bowed to his classmates, who were all much smaller than he was. And all the children, not only the children in Ta-chan's class, bowed back.

At lunchtime Miyazaki went over to the headmaster's house, and all the others followed him. Then what did he do but start to walk into the house with his shoes on! All the children shouted at him, "You've got to take off your shoes!"

Miyazaki seemed startled. "Oh, excuse me," he said, taking them off.

The children began telling him what to do, all talking at once.

"You have to take your shoes off for rooms with tatami-matted floors and for the Assembly Hall. You can keep them on in the classrooms and in the library."

"When you go to Kuhonbutsu Temple you can keep them on in the courtyard but you have to take them off in the temple."

It was fun learning about the differences between living in Japan and living abroad.

Next day Miyazaki brought a big English picture book to school. They all clustered around him at lunchtime to look at the book. They were amazed. They had never seen such a beautiful picture book before. The picture books they knew were only printed in bright reds, greens, and yellows, but this one had pale flesh-colored pinks. As for the blues, they were lovely shades, mixed with white and gray—colors that

でも、白い色や、グレーが、まざっているような、気持ちのいい色で、クレヨンには、ない色だった。二十四色のにもない色で、タアーちゃんだけが持ってる四十八色のクレヨンにだって、ないような色がたくさんあった。みんなは、感心した。それから、次に、絵なんだけど、それは、おむつをした、赤ちゃんが、犬に、おむつを、ひっぱられているところから始まっていた。だけど、みんなが感心したのは、その赤ちゃんが、描(か)いたみたいじゃなく、ピンク色の、やわらかそうな、お尻を出して、本当に、そこにいるみたいだったからだった。そして、第三に、こんな大きくて、厚い、しかも、紙のいいツルツルの絵本を見るのは、初めてだった。トットちゃんは、もちろん、いつものように、抜(ぬ)け目(め)なく、一番、絵本に近く、しかも、宮崎君の、そばに、人なつっこく、くっついていた。

宮崎君は、まず、英語で文章を読んでくれた。それは、とてもとても、なめらかな言葉で、みんなは、うっとりした。それから、宮崎君は、日本語と、格闘(かくとう)を、はじめた。

どっちにしても、宮崎君は、みんなと違うものを、トモエに、運んで来てくれた。

「赤チャンハ、ベイビィー」

宮崎君のいう通り、みんなは、声を出した。

「赤ちゃんは、ベイビィー!!」

それから、また、宮崎君はいう。

「ウツクシハ、ビューティフル」

「美しいは、ビューティフル」

みんながいうと、宮崎君は、すぐに、自分の日本語を訂正(ていせい)した。

「ゴメンナサイ、ウツクシ、チガウ、ウツクシイ?」

こうして、トモエのみんなは、宮崎君とすぐ親しくなった。宮崎君も、毎日、いろんな本を学校に持って来ては、お昼休みに読んでくれた。

didn't exist in crayons. There were lots of colors besides the standard twenty-four in a box of crayons, colors that were not even in Ta-chan's special box of forty-eight. Everyone was impressed. As for the pictures, the first one was of a dog pulling a baby by its diaper. What impressed them was that the baby didn't look as if it was painted but had soft pink skin just like a real baby. They had never seen a picture book that was so big and printed on such lovely, thick, shiny paper. In her usual sociable way, Totto-chan got as close to Miyazaki and the picture book as she could.

Miyazaki read the English text to them. The English language sounded so smooth that they listened enraptured. Then Miyazaki began to grapple with Japanese.

Miyazaki certainly had brought something new and different to the school.

"*Akachan* is baby," he began.

They all repeated it after him. "*Akachan* is baby."

"*UtsuKUshi* is beautiful," Miyazaki said next, stressing the "*ku*" and leaving off the final "*i*."

"*UtsukuSHII* is beautiful," repeated the others.

Miyazaki then realized his Japanese pronunciation had been wrong. "It's *utsukuSHII*, is it? Right?"

Miyazaki and the other children soon became good friends. Every day he brought various books to Tomoe and read them to the others at lunchtime.

It was just as if Miyazaki was their English tutor. At the same time Miyazaki's Japanese quickly improved. And he stopped making blunders like sitting in the

だから、宮崎君は、みんなの、英語の家庭教師という風だった。でも、そのかわり、宮崎君は、みるみるうちに、日本語が、上手になった。そして、床の間にも、腰をかけたり、しなくなった。

トットちゃんたちも、アメリカについて、いろいろ知った。

トモエでは、いま、日本と、アメリカが親しくなり始めていた。

でも、トモエの外では、アメリカは敵国となり、英語は、敵国の言葉ということで、すべての学校の授業から、はずされた。

「アメリカ人は、鬼！」

と、政府は、発表した。このとき、トモエのみんなは、声を揃えて、叫んでいた。

「美しいは、ビューティフル！」

トモエの上を通りすぎる風は暖かく、子供たちは、美しかった。

泰明ちゃんが死んだ

春休みが終わって、初めて学校に集まった日の、朝だった。校庭で、小林先生は、みんなの前に立つと、両手を上着のポケットにいれた、いつもの恰好で、じーっと、立っていた。それから、両手をポケットから出すと、みんなを見た。先生の顔は、泣いているようだった。先生は、ゆっくり、いった。

「泰明ちゃんが、死んだよ。今日、みんなでお葬式に行こう。泰明ちゃんは、みんなの友達だったね。とても残念だよ、先生も。悲しい気持ちで、いっぱいだ……」

そこまでいうと、先生の目のまわりが真赤になり、涙が、先生の目から落ちた。

生徒たちは、みんな呆然として、誰も声を出す子は、いなかった。みんなの胸の中には、それぞれ、泰明ちゃんに対する想いが、

tokonoma, the alcove reserved for hanging-scrolls and ornaments.

Totto-chan and her friends learned lots of things about America. Japan and America were becoming friends at Tomoe. But outside Tomoe, America had become an enemy, and since English had become an enemy language, it was dropped from the curriculum of all the schools.

"Americans are devils," the government announced. But at Tomoe the children kept chanting in chorus, "*Utsukushii* is beautiful." And the breezes that blew across Tomoe were soft and warm, and the children themselves were beautiful.

"Yasuaki-chan's Dead"

It was the first morning of school after the spring vacation. Mr. Kobayashi stood in front of the children assembled on the school grounds, his hands in his pockets as usual. But he didn't say anything for some time. Then he took his hands out of his pockets and looked at the children. He looked as if he had been crying.

"Yasuaki-chan's dead," he said slowly. "We're all going to his funeral today." Then he went on, "You all liked Yasuaki-chan, I know. It's a great shame. I feel terribly sad." He only got that far when his face became bright red and tears welled up in his eyes. The children

こみあげていたに違いなかった。これまでに、こんな悲しい静かさが、トモエの庭を通りすぎたことは、なかった。

トットちゃんは、思った。

「そんなに早く、死んじゃうなんて。春休みの前に、泰明ちゃんが、『読めば?』って貸してくれた〝アンクルトムの小屋〟だって、まだ終わりまで、読めていないくらいなのに」

トットちゃんは、泰明ちゃんの事を、想い出していた。春休みの前に、別れるとき、本を渡してくれた時の、曲がった指のこと。初めて逢った日、

「どうして、そんなふうに歩くの?」

と聞いたトットちゃんに、

「僕、小児麻痺なんだ」

って、やさしく、静かに教えてくれたときの、あの声と、少し笑った顔と。夏の、あの二人だけの大冒険、秘密の木のぼりも（トットちゃんより、年も背も大きかったけど、トットちゃんを信頼し、全部トットちゃんに、まかせた、あのときの、泰明ちゃんのからだの重さも、今は、なつかしかった)。「テレビというものが、アメリカにある」って教えてくれたのも泰明ちゃんだった。

トットちゃんは、泰明ちゃんが好きだった。お休み時間だって、お弁当のときだって、学校が終わって駅まで帰るときだって、いつも一緒だった。なにもかもが、なつかしかった。でも、トットちゃんは、もう二度と泰明ちゃんは、学校に来ないとわかっていた。死ぬって、そういうことなんだから。あの可愛がってた、ひよこだって、死んだら、もう、どんなに呼んでも、動かなかったんだから。

泰明ちゃんのお葬式は、泰明ちゃんの家のある田園調布の、家とは反対側の、テニスコートの近くの教会だった。生徒は、みんな、だまって、自由が丘から一列になって、教会まで歩いていった。いつもはキョロキョロするトットちゃんも、下を見たまま、

were stunned and nobody said a word. They were all thinking about Yasuaki-chan. Never had such a sad quietness passed over the grounds of Tomoe before.

"Imagine dying so soon," thought Totto-chan. "I haven't even finished *Uncle Tom's Cabin* that Yasuaki-chan said I ought to read and lent me before the vacation."

She remembered how crooked his fingers had looked when she and Yasuaki-chan said goodbye before spring vacation and he handed her the book. She recalled the first time she met him, when she had asked, "Why do you walk like that?" and his soft reply, "I had polio." She thought of the sound of his voice and his little smile. And that summer tree-climbing adventure of just the two of them. She remembered with nostalgia how heavy his body had been, and the way he had trusted her implicitly even though he was older and taller. It was Yasuaki-chan who told her they had something in America called television. Totto-chan loved Yasuaki-chan. They had lunch together, spent their breaks together, and walked to the station together after school. She would miss him so much. Totto-chan realized that death meant Yasuaki-chan would never come to school any more. It was like those baby chicks. When they died, no matter how she called to them they never moved again.

Yasuaki-chan's funeral took place at a church near the tennis courts on the opposite side of Denenchofu from where he lived.

ずーっと歩いていた。そして、校長先生から、初めて話を聞いた、さっきと、今の考えが、少し違っていることに気がついた。さっきは、(信じられない)という気持ちと、(なつかしい)という気持ちだったけど、今は、(もう一度だけでいいから、生きてる泰明ちゃんと逢いたい。逢って、話がしたい)という思いで、胸がいっぱいだった。

　教会は、白い百合(ゆり)の花が、たくさんあった。泰明ちゃんの、きれいなお姉さんや、お母さんや、お家の人たちが、黒い洋服を着て、入口の外に立っていた。みんな、トットちゃんたちを見ると、それまでより、もっと泣いた。みんな、白いハンケチを、ぎゅーっと持っていた。トットちゃんは、生まれて初めて、お葬式を見た。お葬式は、悲しいものとわかった。話をしてる人は、誰もいなかった。オルガンが、静かに讃美歌(さんびか)を歌っていた。教会の中は、太陽の光が入って明るいのに、楽しい気持ちは、もう、どこを探しても、ないように思えた。腕に黒いリボンを巻いた男の人が、トモエのみんなに、白い花を一本ずつ渡して、それを持って、一列になって教会に入り、泰明ちゃんの寝てるお棺(かん)の中に、そーっと、それを入れてください、と説明した。

　泰明ちゃんは、お棺の中にいた。花にかこまれて、目をつぶっていた。でも、死んでいても、いつものように、やさしく、利口そうに見えた。トットちゃんは、ひざをつくと、花を、泰明ちゃんの、手のところに置いた。そして、泰明ちゃんの、手に、そっと、さわった。トットちゃんが、何度も何度も、ひっぱった、なつかしい手。汚れて小さいトットちゃんの手にくらべて、泰明ちゃんの手は、真白で、指が長く、大人っぽく見えた。

(じゃね)

　と、トットちゃんは、小さな声で、泰明ちゃんに、いった。

(いつか、うんと大きくなったら、また、どっかで、逢えるんでしょう。そのとき、小児麻痺、なおってると、いいけど)

The children walked there in silence from Jiyugaoka, in single file. Totto-chan didn't look around her as she usually did but kept her eyes on the ground the whole time. She realized she now felt differently from when the headmaster had told them the sad news. Her first reaction was disbelief, and then came sadness. But now all she wanted was to see Yasuaki-chan alive just once more. She wanted to talk to him so much she could hardly bear it.

The church was filled with white lilies. Yasuaki-chan's pretty mother and sister and relatives, all dressed in black, were standing outside the church. When they saw Totto-chan they cried even more, their white handkerchiefs in their hands. It was the first time Totto-chan had been to a funeral, and she realized how sad it was. Nobody talked, and the organ played soft hymn music. The sun was shining and the church was full of light, but there was no happiness in it anywhere. A man with a black armband handed a single white flower to each of the Tomoe children and explained that they were to walk one after the other and place their flower in Yasuaki-chan's coffin.

Yasuaki-chan lay in the coffin with his eyes closed, surrounded by flowers. Although he was dead, he looked as kind and clever as ever. Totto-chan knelt and placed her flower by his hand and gently touched it—the beloved hand she had held so often. His hand was so much whiter than her grubby little hand and his fingers so much longer, like a grown-up's.

それから、トットちゃんは立ち上がり、もう一度、泰明ちゃんを見た。そうだ！　大事なこと忘れていた。
（"アンクルトムの小屋"、もう返せないわね。じゃ、私、あずかっとく。今度、逢うときまで）
そして、トットちゃんは歩きはじめた。そのとき、後ろから、泰明ちゃんの声が聞こえるような気がした。
「トットちゃん！　いろんなこと、楽しかったね。君のこと、忘れないよ」
（そうよ）
トットちゃんは、教会の出口のところで、ふり返って、いった。
（私だって、泰明ちゃんのこと、忘れない！）
明るい春の陽ざしが……、初めて泰明ちゃんと、電車の教室で逢った日と同じ、春の陽ざしが、トットちゃんのまわりを、とりかこんでいた。でも、涙が、いまトットちゃんの頬（ほお）を伝わっているのが、初めて逢った日と、違っていた。

スパイ

泰明（やすあき）ちゃんのことで、トモエのみんなは、ずーっと悲しかった。特にトットちゃんのクラスは、朝、電車の教室で、もう、いくら授業が始まる時間になって泰明ちゃんが来なくても、それは遅刻じゃなくて、絶対に来ないのだ、と馴（な）れるのに時間が、かかった。一クラスが、たったの十人というのは、ふだんはいいけど、こういうときには、（とても、都合が悪い）と、みんなは思った。
「泰明ちゃんがいない」
ということが、どうしても、目で見えてしまうからだった。でも、せめてもの救いは、みんなの座（すわ）る席が決まっていないことだ

" 'Bye now," she whispered to Yasuaki-chan. "Maybe we'll meet again somewhere when we're much older. And maybe your polio will be cured by then."

Then Totto-chan got up and looked at Yasuaki-chan once more. "Oh yes, I forgot," she said, "*Uncle Tom's Cabin*. I shan't be able to return it to you now, shall I? I'll keep it for you, until we meet next time."

As she started walking away, she was sure she heard his voice behind her, "Totto-chan, we had a lot of fun together, didn't we? I'll never forget you. Never."

When Totto-chan reached the entrance, she turned around. "I'll never forget you either," she said.

The spring sunshine shone softly just as it had on the day she first met Yasuaki-chan in the classroom-in-the-train. But unlike that day, her cheeks were wet with tears.

A Spy

The children at Tomoe were sad for a long time, thinking about Yasuaki-chan, particularly so in the morning, when it was time to start class. It took a while for the children to get used to the fact that Yasuaki was not just late, but wasn't ever coming again. Small classes might be nice, but at times like this it made things much harder. Yasuaki-chan's absence was so conspicuous. The only saving grace was the fact that seats were not assigned. If he had had a regular desk, its being

った。もし、泰明ちゃんの席が決まっていて、そこが、いつまでも空いてるとしたら、それは、とても、つらいことだったに違いない。でも、トモエでは、毎日、好きな席に自由に座っていい、というきまりだったから、そこのところは、ありがたかった。

このところ、トットちゃんは、自分が大きくなったら、「なにになろうか?」という事を考えるようになっていた。もっと小さい頃は、チンドン屋さんとか、バレリーナと思っていたし、初めてトモエに来た日には、駅で、電車の切符を売る人もいい、と思った。でも、いまは、もう少し、女らしく、なにか、かわっていることを仕事にする人になりたい、と考えていた。

(看護婦さんもいいな……)

と、トットちゃんは、思いついた。

(でも……)

と、すぐにトットちゃんは思い出した。

(この前、病院にいる兵隊さんをお見舞いに行ったとき、看護婦さんは、注射なんか、してあげてたじゃない? あれは、ちょっと、むずかしそうだ……)

「そうかといって、なにがいいかなあ……」

いいかけて、突然、トットちゃんは、うれしさで、いっぱいになった。

「なんだ、ちゃんと、なるもの、前に決めてたんだ!」

それからトットちゃんは、泰(たい)ちゃんのそばに行った。ちょうど泰ちゃんは、教室で、アルコール・ランプに火をつけたところだった。トットちゃんは、得意そうにいった。

「私、スパイになろうと思うんだ!」

泰ちゃんは、アルコール・ランプの炎(ほのお)から、目をトットちゃんにむけると、じっと、トットちゃんの顔を見た。それから、少し考えるように、目を窓の外にやり、それから、トットちゃんのほうにむきなおると、響(ひび)きのある利口そうな声で、そして、トット

vacant would have been awful.

Recently Totto-chan had begun to think about what she would like to be when she grew up. When she was younger she thought she wanted to be a street musician or a ballerina, and the day she first arrived at Tomoe she thought it would be nice to be a ticket seller at a station. But now she thought she would like to do some kind of work that was unusual but a little more feminine. It might be rather nice to be a nurse, she thought. But she suddenly remembered that when she had visited the wounded soldiers in the hospital she had noticed nurses doing things like giving injections, and that might be rather difficult. So what should she do? Suddenly she was transported with joy.

"Why, of course! I've already decided what I am going to be!"

She went over to Tai-chan, who had just lit his alcohol burner.

"I'm thinking of becoming a spy," she said proudly.

ちゃんにわかりやすいように、ゆっくりと、いった。

「スパイになるにはね、頭がよくなくちゃ、なれないんだよ。それに、いろんな国の言葉だって出来なくちゃなれないし……」

そこまでいうと、泰ちゃんは、ちょっと、息をついた。そして、目をそらさずに、はっきりと、トットちゃんを見て、いった。

「第一、女のスパイは、顔がきれいじゃなくちゃ、なれないんだよ」

トットちゃんは、だんだん目を泰ちゃんから床に落とし、顔も、少し、うつむくような形になった。それから泰ちゃんは、少し間をおき、今度は、トットちゃんから目をそらして、小さな声で、考えながら、いった。

「それに、おしゃべりの子は、スパイには、なれないんじゃないかなあ……」

トットちゃんは、びっくりした。それは、スパイになることを反対されたからじゃなかった。泰ちゃんのいうことが、すべて正しいからだった。すべてが、思いあたることだった。

トットちゃんは、どこをとっても、スパイになれる才能はない、と、自分でも、よくわかった。泰ちゃんが、意地悪でいってるんじゃないことは勿論だった。スパイは、あきらめるよりしか、なかった。やっぱり相談してよかった。

（それにしても！）

と、トットちゃんは、心の中で考えた。

（すごい！　泰ちゃんは、私と同じ年なのに、こんなに、いろんなことが、よくわかっているなんて……）

もし、泰ちゃんが、トットちゃんに、

「僕、物理学者になろうと思うんだけど！」

なんていったら、一体、どんなことを、いってあげられるだろうか。

「アルコール・ランプに、マッチで上手に火がつけられるもの、

Tai-chan turned away from the flame and looked at Totto-chan's face for some time. Then he gazed out of the window for a while, as if he were thinking it over, before turning to Totto-chan again to say in his intelligent, resonant voice, slowly and simply, so she would understand, "You have to be clever to be a spy. Besides that, you've got to know a lot of languages."

Tai-chan paused a moment for breath. Then he looked straight at her and said bluntly, "In the first place, a lady spy has to be beautiful."

Totto-chan slowly lowered her eyes from Tai-chan's gaze and hung her head. After a pause, Tai-chan said thoughtfully in a low voice, this time without looking at Totto-chan, "And besides, I don't think a chatterbox could be a spy."

Totto-chan was dumbfounded. Not because he was against her being a spy. But because everything Tai-chan said was true. They were all things she had suspected. She realized then that in every respect she lacked the talents a spy needed. She knew, of course, that Tai-chan had not said those things out of spite. There was nothing to do but give up the idea. It was just as well she had talked it over with him.

"Goodness me," she thought to herself, "Tai-chan's the same age as I am and yet he knows so much more."

Supposing Tai-chan told her he was thinking of being a physicist. What on earth would she be able to say in reply?

She might say, "Well, you're good at lighting alcohol

なれると思うわ……」
　でも、これじゃ、ちょっと子供っぽいかなあ。
「英語で、狐(きつね)はフォックスで、靴はシューズ、って知ってるんだもの、なれるんじゃないの?」
　これでも、充分じゃ、なさそうだ。
(でも、泰ちゃんなら、いずれにしても、利口な人のする仕事にむいている)
　と、トットちゃんは、思った。だから、トットちゃんは、だまって、フラスコの泡(あわ)を見つめてる泰ちゃんに、やさしく、いった。
「ありがとう。スパイはやめる。でも、泰ちゃんは、きっと偉(えら)い人になるわ」
　泰ちゃんは、口の中で、なにか、モゾモゾいうと、頭をかきながら、開いた本の中に、頭を、うずめてしまった。
(スパイもだめなら、なにになったら、いいのかな?)
　トットちゃんは、泰ちゃんと並んで、アルコール・ランプの炎を見つめながら、考えていた。

ヴァイオリン

　戦争は、いつの間にか、トットちゃんたちの生活の中に、その恐ろしい姿を見せ始めていた。
　毎日、お隣りや、ご近所の、おじさんやお兄さんが、日の丸の旗と、「ばんざーい !!　ばんざーい !!」に送られて、いなくなっていった。たべものは、どんどん、お店から姿を消した。トモエのお弁当の、〝海のものと、山のもの〞も、実行が難しくなり、それでも、ママたちは、なんとか、「のりと梅干」で、海と山にしていたけど、だんだん、それすらも、大変になってきた。なにもかもが配給になった。お菓子なんて、もう、どこを探しても、見

burners with a match." But that would sound too childish.

"Well, you know that *kitsune* is 'fox' in English and *kutsu* are 'shoes,' so I think you could be a physicist." No, that wasn't good enough, either.

In any event, she was quite sure Tai-chan was destined to do something brilliant. So she just said sweetly to Tai-chan, who was watching the bubbles form in his flask, "Thank you. I shan't be a spy, then. But I'm sure you will become somebody important."

Tai-chan mumbled something, scratched his head, and buried himself in the book that lay open before him.

If she couldn't be a spy, then what could she be, wondered Totto-chan, as she stood beside Tai-chan and stared at the flame on his burner.

Daddy's Violin

Before they knew it, the war with all its horrors was beginning to make itself felt in the life of Totto-chan and her family. Every day men and boys from the neighborhood were sent off with waving flags and shouts of "*Banzai*!" Foodstuffs rapidly disappeared one after the other from the shops. It became harder to comply with the Tomoe lunchtime rule of "something from the ocean and something from the hills." Mother was making do with seaweed and pickled plums, but

ることは出来なかった。

トットちゃんは、家に帰る駅の、一つ手前の、〝大岡山〟の駅の階段の下に、お金を入れると、キャラメルが出て来る機械が置いてあるのを知っていた。その機械の上のほうには、おいしそうな、キャラメルの絵が描いてあった。キャラメルは、小さい箱が五銭で、長い箱のが、十銭だった。でも、その機械の中には、もう、ずーっと前から、キャラメルは、入っていなかった。だから、どんなにお金を入れても、叩いても、何も出て来ないのだった。でも、トットちゃんは、みんなより、しつこかった。

「もしかすると、一箱くらい、残っているのが出てくるんじゃないか?」

「どっかに、ひっかかっているかも知れない!」

そう思ったから、毎日、わざわざ電車を途中下車しては、五銭と十銭を入れて、ためしてみるのだった。でも、いつも、お金だけがチャリン! と音をたてて、もどって来た。

そんなとき、パパに誰かから、話があった。それは、軍需工場という、兵器とか、そのほか戦争で使うものを作っているところに行って、軍歌をヴァイオリンで弾くと、帰りに、お砂糖とか、お米とか、ヨーカンなどが、もらえる、という、ふつうなら、耳よりの話だった。特にその頃、〝優秀音楽家〟ということで表彰されたパパは、ヴァイオリニストとして有名だったから、おみやげも、たくさんいただけるだろうと、話を持って来た、その人は、いった。

ママがパパに聞いた。

soon even that became difficult to get. Just about everything was rationed. There were no sweets to be found, no matter how hard you searched.

Totto-chan knew about a vending machine under the stairs at Ookayama, the station before hers, where you could get a packet of caramels if you put money in the slot. There was a very appetizing picture on top of the machine. You could get a small packet for five sen and a big one for ten. But the machine had been empty for a long time now. Nothing would come out no matter how much money you put in or how hard you banged. Totto-chan was more persistent than most.

"Maybe there's still one packet in there somewhere," she thought. "Maybe it's caught inside."

So every day she got off the train at the stop before hers and tried putting five- and ten-sen coins into the machine. But all she got back was her money. It fell out with a clatter.

About that time, someone told Daddy what most people would have thought welcome news. If he went and played popular wartime music on his violin at something called a munitions factory—where they made weapons and other things used in war—he would be given sugar and rice and other treats. Since Daddy, who had recently been awarded a prestigious musical decoration, was well known as a violinist, the friend told him he would certainly be given a lot of extra presents.

"What do you think?" Mother asked Daddy. "Are you going to do it?"

「どうする？　行ってみる？」

たしかに、演奏会の数は、へっていた。第一、出征していく人がふえてきて、オーケストラのメンバーも揃っていなかった。NHKの放送の仕事も、ほとんどが戦争のことになっていて、パパたちの音楽の仕事は少なかった。だから、今では、こういう仕事も、有難い、はずだった。

でも、パパは、ママの質問に、時間をかけて、答えた。

「……僕のヴァイオリンで、軍歌は、弾きたくない」

ママは、いった。

「そうね。やめれば？　たべものだって、なんとか、なるわよ」

パパだって、トットちゃんが、ろくなたべものしかなくて、毎日、キャラメルの販売機に、むなしく、お金を入れてることは、知っていた。だから、ちょっと行って、軍歌を弾いて、おみやげをもらって帰れば、どんなに家の中が、たのしくなるか、そして、トットちゃんにも、たべものを、お腹いっぱい、たべさせてやれるだろうことは、わかっていた。

でも、それより以上に、パパには、自分の音楽が大切だった。ママにも、それが、よくわかっていたので、

「ちょっと行って来てくだされば、いいのに……」

なんて、いわなかったのだった。

パパは、トットちゃんに、悲しそうに、いった。

「ごめんね、トット助！」

トットちゃんには、まだ芸術とか、思想とか、また、仕事のことは、よくわからなかった。でも、パパが本当にヴァイオリンが好きで、そのために、勘当というのになって、家や、親戚の、のけものにされたことや、あと、いろんな大変なことがあったけど、それでも、絶対にやめなかったってこと、知っていたから、いやなものは、弾かないほうが、いい、と思った。だから、トットちゃんは、パパのまわりを、とびはねながら、元気にいった。

Concerts were certainly becoming scarce. In the first place, more and more musicians were being called up and the orchestra was short of players. Radio broadcasts were almost entirely given over to programs connected with the war, so there was not much work for Daddy and his colleagues. He ought to have welcomed the opportunity to play anything.

Daddy thought for some time before replying. "I don't want to play that sort of thing on my violin."

"I think you're right," said Mother. "I would refuse. We'll get food somehow."

Daddy knew Totto-chan had barely enough to eat and was vainly putting money in the caramel vending machine every day. He also knew that the gifts of food he would receive for playing a few wartime tunes would be very handy for his family. But Daddy valued his music even more. Mother knew that, too, and so she never urged him to do it. "Forgive me, Totsky!" said Daddy, sadly.

Totto-chan was too young to know about art and ideology and work. But she did know that Daddy loved the violin so much he had been something called "disowned," and many of his family and relatives did not speak to him any more. He had had a hard time, but he had refused to give up the violin all the same. So Totto-chan thought it quite right for him not to play something he didn't like. Totto-chan skipped about around Daddy and said cheerfully, "I don't mind. Because I love your violin, too."

「平気！　私もパパのヴァイオリン、好きだもの！」
　だけど、次の日も、トットちゃんは、また、大岡山の駅で降りて、キャラメルの出口を、のぞきこんだ。
　決して、何も出て来るはずのない、出口を。

約　束

　お弁当がすんで、みんなで、丸く並べた机や椅子を片づけると、講堂は広くなる。トットちゃんは、
「今日は、まっ先に、校長先生に、よじのぼろう」
　と決めていた。いつもそう思ってるんだけど、ちょっと油断すると、もう、誰かが、講堂のまん中に、あぐらをかいてる先生の足の間に入りこんでいて、背中には、二人ぐらい、よじのぼって、さわいでいて、そして校長先生は、
「おい、よせよ、よせよ！」
　と真っ赤な顔で笑いながらいうんだけど、その子たちは、一度、占領した先生の体から、はなれまい、と必死だった。だから、ちょっと遅くなると、もう、小柄な校長先生の体は、大混雑なのだった。でも、今日、トットちゃんは決めたから、先生が来る前から、その場所……講堂のまん中……に、立って待っていた。そして、先生が歩いてくると、こう叫んだ。
「ねえ、先生、はなし、はなし!!」
　先生は、あぐらをかくために、すわりながら、うれしそうに聞いた。
「なんだい？　はなしって」
　トットちゃんは、数日前から、心に思ってることを、いま、はっきり先生に、いおうとしていた。先生が、あぐらをかくと、突然、トットちゃんは、（今日は、よじのぼるのは、やめよう）と思

But the next day Totto-chan again got off at Ookayama and peered into the hole in the vending machine. It was unlikely that anything would come out, but she still kept hoping.

The Promise

After lunch, when the children put away the chairs and desks that had been arranged in a circle, the Assembly Hall seemed quite spacious.

"Today, I'm going to be the first to climb on the headmaster's back," decided Totto-chan.

That's what she always wanted to do, but if she hesitated for a moment, someone else would have already climbed into his lap as he sat cross-legged in the middle of the Assembly Hall, and at least two others would be scrambling onto his back, clamoring for his attention.

"Hey, stop it, stop it," the headmaster would remonstrate, red in the face with laughter, but once they had occupied his back, the children were determined not to give up their position. So if you were the least bit slow, you'd find the headmaster's back very crowded. But this time Totto-chan made up her mind to be there first and was already waiting in the middle of the Assembly Hall when the headmaster arrived. As he approached, she shouted to him, "Sir, I've got something to tell you."

"What is it, then?" asked the headmaster delight-

った。こういう話は、ちゃんと、向かいあうのが、適当、という風に考えたからだった。だから、トットちゃんは、先生に向かいあい、くっついて正座した。そして、顔を少しまげた。小さいときから、「いいお顔！」と、ママなんかにいわれている顔をした。それは、歯を少し見せて笑う、よそゆきの顔だった。この顔のときは、自信があり、いい子だと、自分でも思っているときだった。

先生は、膝を、のり出すようにして聞いた。

「なんだい？」

トットちゃんは、まるで、先生の、お姉さんか、お母さんのように、ゆっくりと、やさしく、いった。

「私、大きくなったら、この学校の先生に、なってあげる。必ず」

先生は、笑うかと思ったら、そうじゃなく、まじめな顔をして、トットちゃんに聞いた。

「約束するかい？」

先生の顔は、本当に、トットちゃんに、「なってほしい」と思っているように見えた。トットちゃんは、大きくうなずくと、

「約束！」

と、いった。いいながら、（本当に。絶対に、なる！）と自分にも、いいきかせた。

この瞬間、はじめて、トモエに来た朝のこと……随分むかしに思えるけど、あの一年生のときの……はじめて、先生に、校長室で逢ったときのことを思い出していた。先生は、四時間も、自分の話を、ちゃんと聞いてくれた。あとにも、先にも、トットちゃんの話を、四時間も、聞いてくれた、大人は、いなかった。そして、話が終わったとき、

「今日から、君は、この学校の生徒だよ」

って、いってくださったときの、先生の、あったかい声。いま、トットちゃんは、あのときより、もっと、

edly, as he sat down on the floor and started to cross his legs.

Totto-chan wanted to tell him what she had decided after several days' thought. When the headmaster had crossed his legs, Totto-chan suddenly decided against climbing on his back. What she had to say would be more appropriate said face to face. So she sat down very close to him, facing him, and tilted her head a little with a smile that Mother had called her "nice face" ever since she was small. It was her "Sunday best" face. She felt confident when she smiled like that, her mouth slightly open, and she herself believed she was a good girl.

The headmaster looked at her expectantly. "What is it?" he asked again, leaning forward.

Totto-chan said sweetly and slowly, in a big-sisterly or motherly way, "I'd like to teach at this school when I grow up. I really would."

Totto-chan expected the headmaster to smile, but instead, he asked in all seriousness, "Promise?"

He really seemed to want her to do it.

Totto-chan nodded her head vigorously and said, "I promise," determining in her heart to become a teacher there without fail.

At that moment she was thinking about the morning when she first came to Tomoe as a first grader and met the headmaster in his office. It seemed a long time ago. He had listened patiently to her for four hours. She thought of the warmth in his voice when he had

（小林先生は、大好きだ）
　と思っていた。そして、先生のために働くこと、先生のためになる事なら、なんでもしようと心に決めていた。
　先生は、トットちゃんの決心を聞くと、いつものように、歯の抜けた口を、恥ずかしそうにしないで、見せて、うれしそうに、笑った。
　トットちゃんは、先生の目の前に、小指をつき出した。
「約束！」
　先生も小指を出した。短いけど、力強そうな、信頼出来そうな、先生の小指だった。トットちゃんと、先生は、指きりゲンマン！をした。先生は笑っていた。トットちゃんも、先生がうれしそうなのを見て、安心して、笑った。
　トモエの先生になる!!
　なんて、すばらしいことだろう。
（私が、先生になったら……）
　トットちゃんが、いろいろ想像して、思いついたことは、次のようなことだった。
「勉強は、あんまり、やらないでさ。運動会とか、ハンゴウスイサンとか、野宿（のじゅく）とか、いっぱいやって、それから、散歩！」
　小林先生は、よろこんでいた。大きくなったトットちゃんを想像するのは、むずかしかったけど、きっと、トモエの先生になれるだろう、と考えていた。そして、どの子も、トモエを卒業した子は、小さい子供の心を忘れるはずはないのだから、どの子も、トモエの先生になれるはずだと考えていた。
　日本の空に、いつアメリカの飛行機が爆弾をつんで、姿を見せるか、それは、時間の問題、といわれているとき、この、電車が校庭に並んでいるトモエ学園の中では、校長先生と、生徒が、十年以上も先の、約束を、していた。

said to her, after she had finished talking, "Now you're a pupil of this school." She loved Mr. Kobayashi even more than she had then. And she was determined to work for him and do anything she could to help him.

When she had promised, he smiled delightedly—as usual, showing no embarrassment about his missing teeth. Totto-chan held out her little finger. The headmaster did the same. His little finger looked strong—you could put your faith in it. Totto-chan and the headmaster then made a pledge in the time-honored Japanese way by linking little fingers. The headmaster was smiling. Totto-chan smiled, too, reassured. She was going to be a teacher at Tomoe! What a wonderful thought.

"When I'm a teacher . . . ," she mused. And these were the things that Totto-chan imagined: not too much study; lots of Sports Days, field kitchens, camping, and walks!

The headmaster was delighted. It was hard to imagine Totto-chan grown-up, but he was sure she could be a Tomoe teacher. He thought the Tomoe children would all make good teachers since they were likely to remember what it was like being a child.

There at Tomoe, the headmaster and one of his pupils were making a solemn promise about something that lay ten years or more in the future, when everyone was saying it was only a matter of time before American airplanes loaded with bombs appeared in the skies over Japan.

ロッキーが、いなくなった

たくさんの兵隊さんが死に、たべものが無くなり、みんなが恐ろしい気持ちで暮らしていても、夏は、いつもと同じように、やって来た。太陽は、戦争に勝ってる国にも、負けてる国にも、同じように、光を送って来た。

トットちゃんは、いま、鎌倉(かまくら)の、おじさまの家から、夏休みが終わるので東京の自分の家に帰って来たところだった。

トモエでの、楽しかった野宿(のじゅく)や、土肥(とい)温泉への旅などは、もう、何も出来なかった。学校のみんなと一緒のあの夏休みは、もう、二度と味わえそうになかった。そして、毎年、いとこたちと過ごす鎌倉の家も、いつもの夏とは、全く違っていた。毎年、みんなが、こわくて泣いちゃうくらい上手に、怪談をしてくれた親戚の大きいお兄さんが、兵隊に行ってしまった。だから、もう、怪談は、無しだった。それから、アメリカでの、いろんな生活の話を、本当か嘘か、わからないくらい面白く話してくれる、おじさまも、戦地だった。この、おじさまは、第一級の報道カメラマンで、名前を、田口修治といった。

でも、「日本ニュース」のニューヨーク支社長や「アメリカ・メトロニュース」の極東代表をしてからは、シュウ・タグチ、としてのほうが有名だった。この人は、トットちゃんのパパのすぐ上のお兄さんで、本当の兄弟だけど、パパだけが、パパのお母さんの家の姓をついだので、名前が違うわけで、本当なら、パパも、「田口さん」になるはずだったんだけど。

この、おじさまの写した「ラバウル攻防戦」とか、その他の、いろんなニュース映画は、次々と映画館で上映されていたけど、戦地から、フィルムだけが送られて来るのだから、おばさまや、いとこたちは、心配していた。なぜって、報道カメラマンは、いつも、みんなの危険なところを撮(と)るのだから、みんなより、もっと先に行って、ふり返って待っていて写さなければ、ならないか

Rocky Disappears

Lots of soldiers had died, food had become scarce, everyone was living in fear—but summer came as usual. And the sun shone on the nations that were winning as well as on the nations that weren't.

Totto-chan had just returned to Tokyo from her uncle's house in Kamakura.

There was no camping now at Tomoe and no more lovely visits to hot spring resorts. It seemed as if the children would never be able to enjoy a summer vacation as happy as that one. Totto-chan always spent the summer with her cousins at their house in Kamakura, but this year it had been different. An older boy, a relative who used to tell them scary ghost stories, had been called up and had gone to the war. So there were no more ghost stories. And her uncle who used to tell them such interesting tales about his life in America—they never knew whether they were true or not—was at the front. His name was Shuji Taguchi, and he was a top-ranking cameraman.

After serving as bureau chief of Nihon News in New York and as Far East representative of American Metro-News, he was better known as Shu Taguchi. He was Daddy's elder brother, though Daddy had taken his mother's family name in order to perpetuate it. Otherwise Daddy's surname would have been Taguchi, too. Films Uncle Shuji had shot, such as "The Battle of Rabaul," were being shown at movie theaters, but all he sent from the front were his films, so Totto-chan's

らだった。あとから行ったのでは、みんなの後ろ姿しか、撮れないからだった。道がなければ、みんなより先に、道のないところを、かきわけて、先か、または、横に行って撮るのが仕事だった。みんなの作ってくれた道を行ったのでは、こういう戦争中のニュースは撮れないのだと、親戚の大人たちは、話していた。鎌倉の海岸も、なんとなく、心細そうだった。

そんな中で、おかしかったのは、この、おじさまの家の一番上の男の子の、寧(や)っちゃん、という子だった。トットちゃんより、一歳くらい下だったけど、寝る前に、トットちゃんや、他の子供たちの寝るカヤの中で、「天皇陛下(へいか)、ばんざい !!」といって、ばったり倒れて戦死する兵隊さんの、まねを、何度も真剣にやるんだけど、それをやった晩は、なぜか、必ず、ねぼけて、夜中に、縁側から落ちて、大さわぎに、なるのだった。

トットちゃんのママは、パパの仕事があるので、パパと東京だった。

さて、夏休みが終わる今日、ちょうど、東京に帰る大きい親戚のお姉さんが来ていたので、トットちゃんは、いま、家まで連れて帰って来ていただいたところだった。

家に帰ったトットちゃんは、まず、いつものように、犬のロッキーを探した。でも、ロッキーは、どこにも見えなかった。家の中には勿論、庭にも、パパの趣味の蘭(らん)なんかがあった温室にも。トットちゃんは心配になった。いつもなら、トットちゃんが、家の近くまで帰って来ただけで、どっかから、飛び出して来るロッキーなんだから……。トットちゃんは、家を出て、ずーっと、外の通りのほうまで行って、名前を呼んだけど、どこからも、あの、なつかしい目や耳や、しっぽは見えなかった。トットちゃんは、自分が外に出ているうちに、家に帰ってるかも知れないと思って、走って帰ってみた。でも、まだ帰って来ていなかった。トットちゃんは、ママに聞いた。

aunt and cousins were worried about him. War photographers always showed the troops in dangerous positions, so they had to be ahead of the troops to show them advancing. That was what Totto-chan's grown-up relatives had been saying.

Even the beach at Kamakura somehow seemed forlorn that summer. Yat-chan was funny, though, in spite of it all. He was Uncle Shuji's eldest son. Yat-chan was about a year younger than Totto-chan. The children all slept together under one large mosquito net, and before he went to sleep, Yat-chan used to shout "Long Live the Emperor!" then fall like a soldier who had been shot and pretend to be dead. He would do it over and over again. The funny thing was that whenever he did this, he invariably walked in his sleep and fell off the porch, causing a great fuss.

Totto-chan's mother had stayed in Tokyo with Daddy, who had work to do. Now that summer vacation was over, Totto-chan had been brought back to Tokyo by the sister of the boy who used to tell ghost stories.

As usual on arriving at home, the first thing Totto-chan did was look for Rocky. But he was nowhere to be found. He wasn't in the house and he wasn't in the garden. Nor was he in the greenhouse where Daddy grew orchids. Totto-chan was worried, since Rocky normally came out to meet her long before she even reached the house. Totto-chan went out of the house and down the road, calling his name, but there was no sign of those

「ロッキーは?」
さっきから、トットちゃんが走りまわっているのを、知っているはずのママは、だまっていた。トットちゃんは、ママのスカートを引っぱって聞いた。
「ねえ、ロッキーは?」
ママは、とても答えにくそうに、いった。
「いなくなったの」
トットちゃんは、信じられなかった。
(いなくなった?)
「いつ?」
トットちゃんは、ママの顔を見て聞いた。
ママは、どうしたらいいか……という風な悲しい感じで、いった。
「あなたが、鎌倉に出かけて、すぐ」
それから、ママは、いそいで、つけ足した。
「随分さがしたのよ。遠くまで行ってみたし、みんなにも聞いてみたけど、どこにも、いないのよ。あなたに、なんていったら、いいか、ママは考えていたんだけど……。ごめんなさいね……」
そのとき、トットちゃんは、はっきりと、わかった。
ロッキーは、死んだんだ。
(ママは、私を悲しませないように、いってるけど、ロッキーは死んだんだ)
トットちゃんには、はっきりしていた。今まで、トットちゃんが、どんなに遠くに出かけても、ロッキーは、絶対に、遠出をすることは、なかった。なぜなら、トットちゃんが、必ず帰って来ることを知っていたからだった。
(私に、なにもいわずに、ロッキーが出かけて行くなんて、絶対に、ない)
それは、確信に近かった。
トットちゃんは、それ以上、ママに何もいわなかった。ママの

beloved eyes, ears, or tail. Totto-chan thought he might have gone back while she was out looking for him, so she hurriedly ran home to see. But he wasn't there.

"Where's Rocky?" she asked Mother.

Mother must have known Totto-chan was running everywhere looking for Rocky, but she didn't say a word.

"Where's Rocky?" Totto-chan asked again, pulling Mother's skirt.

Mother seemed to find it difficult to reply. "He disappeared," she said.

Totto-chan refused to believe it. How could he have disappeared? "When?" she asked, looking Mother in the face.

Mother seemed at a loss for words. "Just after you left for Kamakura," she began, sadly. Then she hurriedly continued, "We looked for him. We went everywhere. And we asked everybody. But we couldn't find him. I've been wondering how to tell you. I'm terribly sorry."

Then the truth dawned on Totto-chan. Rocky must have died. "Mother doesn't want me to be sad," she thought, "but Rocky's dead."

It was quite clear to Totto-chan. Up till now, no matter how long Totto-chan was gone, Rocky never went far from the house. He always knew she would come back. "Rocky would never go off like that without telling me," she thought to herself. It was a strong conviction.

気持ちは、充分に、わかったからだった。トットちゃんは、下をむいたまま、いった。
「どこに行ったのかなあー」
そういうのが、せい一杯で、トットちゃんは、二階の自分の部屋に、かけこんだ。ロッキーのいない家の中は、よその家のようにさえ、思えた。トットちゃんは、部屋に入ると、泣きそうになるのを我慢して、もう一度、考えてみた。それは、ロッキーに対して、なにか、〝意地悪なこととか、家を出ていくようなことをしなかったか、どうか?〟ということだった。
小林先生は、いつも、トモエの生徒に、いっていた。
「動物を、だましちゃ、いけないよ。君たちを信じてる動物を、裏切るようなことを、しちゃ、可哀そうだからね。犬なんかに〝お手をしたら、お菓子をやるよ〟、なんて、いって、お手をさせて、何もやらなかったりするなよ。犬は、君たちを信じなくなるし、性格が悪くなるからね」
このことを守っているトットちゃんは、ロッキーを、だますようなことは、していなかったし、思いあたることは、まったく、なかった。
そのとき、トットちゃんは、床においてある、熊(くま)のぬいぐるみの足に、くっついているものを見た。いままで、我慢していたトットちゃんは、それを見ると、声をあげて、泣いた。それは、ロッキーの、薄茶色の毛だった。トットちゃんが、鎌倉に出発する朝、ロッキーと、ここで、ふざけて、ころがったりしたとき、ロッキーから、抜け落ちた毛だった。その、ほんの数本の、シェパードの毛を、手に握りしめたまま、トットちゃんは、いつまでも、いつまでも、泣いた。涙も、泣く声も、どうしても、止まらなかった。
泰明(やすあき)ちゃんに続いて、トットちゃんは、また、親友を、なくしてしまった。

But Totto-chan did not discuss it with Mother. She knew how Mother must feel. "I wonder where he went," was all she said, keeping her eyes lowered.

It was all she could do to say that much, and then she ran upstairs to her room. Without Rocky, the house didn't seem like their house at all. When she got to her room, she tried hard not to cry and thought about it once more. She wondered whether she had done anything mean to Rocky—anything that would make him want to leave.

"Never tease animals," Mr. Kobayashi always told the children at Tomoe. "It's cruel to betray animals when they trust you. Don't make a dog beg and then not give it anything. The dog won't trust you any more and might develop a bad nature."

Totto-chan always obeyed these rules. She had never deceived Rocky. She had done nothing wrong that she could think of.

Just then Totto-chan noticed something clinging to the leg of her teddy bear on the floor. She had managed not to cry until then, but when she saw it she burst into tears. It was a little tuft of Rocky's light brown hair. It must have come off when the two of them had rolled about on the floor, playing, the morning she left for Kamakura. With those few little German shepherd hairs clutched in her hand, she cried and cried. Her tears and her sobbing just wouldn't stop.

First Yasuaki-chan and now Rocky. Totto-chan had lost another friend.

茶話会

　トモエで、みんなから人気のある、用務員の良ちゃんが、とうとう出征することになった。生徒より、ずーっと、大人で、おじさんだったけど、みんなは、親しみをこめて、
「良ちゃん!!」
　と呼んだ。そして、良ちゃんは、みんなが困ったときの、助けの神様だった。良ちゃんは、なんでも出来た。いつも、だまって笑っているけど、困って助けの要る子の必要とするものを、すぐ、わかってくれた。トットちゃんが、トイレの汲み取り口の、地面にあるコンクリートのフタが、開いているのに気がつかなくて、遠くから走ってきて、胸までドップリ、落っこちたときも、すぐ助けてくれて、いやがりもしないで洗ってくれたのも、良ちゃんだった。
　小林校長先生は、出征して行く良ちゃんのために、
「茶話会をしよう」
　といった。
「サワカイ?」
　なんだろう?　みんなは、すっかり、うれしくなった。なんにも

The Tea Party

Ryo-chan, the janitor at Tomoe, whom all the children liked so much, was finally called up. He was a grown-up, but they all called him by his childish nickname. Ryo-chan was a sort of guardian angel who always came to the rescue and helped when anyone was in trouble. Ryo-chan could do anything. He never said much, and only smiled, but he always knew just what to do. When Totto-chan fell into the cesspool, it was Ryo-chan who came to her rescue straight away, and washed her off without so much as a grumble.

"Let's give Ryo-chan a rousing, send-off tea party" said the headmaster.

"A tea party?"

Green tea is drunk many times during the day in Japan, but it is not associated with entertaining—except ceremonial powdered tea, a different beverage altogether. A "tea party" would be something new at Tomoe. But the children liked the idea. They loved doing things they'd never done before. The children didn't know it, but the headmaster had invented a new word, *sawakai* (tea party), instead of the usual *sobetsukai* (farewell party) on purpose. A farewell party sounded too sad, and the older children would understand that it might really be farewell if Ryo-chan got killed and didn't come back. But nobody had ever been to a tea party before, so they were all excited.

After school, Mr. Kobayashi had the children arrange the desks in a circle in the Assembly Hall just

知らないことを知るのは、うれしいことだから。勿論、子供たちには、「送別会」とせずに、「茶話会」とした、小林先生の配慮までは、わかっていなかった。送別会といったら、(それは、悲しい)と、始めから、大きい子には、わかってしまうに違いなかった。でも、「茶話会」は、誰も知らなかったから、みんな興奮した。

　放課後、小林先生は、みんなに講堂に、お弁当のときのように、机を、まるく並べるように、といった。みんなが、まるくなって、すわると、小林先生は、みんなに、スルメの焼いた細いのを、一本ずつ、配った。これでも当時としては、大御馳走だった。それから、先生は、良ちゃんと並んですわると、コップに入った、少しのお酒を、良ちゃんの前においた。出征していく人だけに、配給になる、お酒だった。校長先生は、いった。

「トモエで初めての、茶話会だ。楽しい会にしようね。みんな、良ちゃんに、いいたいことがあったら、いってください。良ちゃんだけじゃなく、生徒に、いってもいいよ。一人ずつ、まん中に立って、さあ、始めよう」

　スルメを、学校でたべるのも初めてなら、良ちゃんが、みんなと一緒にすわるのも、それから、お酒をチビチビやる、良ちゃんを見るのも初めてだった。

　次々に、みんなは、良ちゃんのほうをむいて立つと、考えをいった。始めのうちの、誰かは、「いってらっしゃい」とか、「病気しないでね」、とか、いう風だったけど、トットちゃんのクラスの右田君が、

「今度、田舎から、葬式まんじゅう、持ってきて、みんなにあげます!!」

　なんて、いった頃から、もう、大笑いになった。(だって、右田君は、もう一年も前から、そのまえに田舎で喰べた、この葬式まんじゅうの味が忘れられなくて、ことあるごとに、みんなに、「く

as at lunchtime. When they were all sitting in a circle, he gave each one a single thin strip of roasted dried squid to have with their green tea. Even that was a great luxury in those wartime days. Then he sat down next to Ryo-chan and placed a glass before him with a little saké in it. It was a ration obtainable only for those leaving for the front.

"This is the first tea party at Tomoe," said the headmaster. "Let's all have a good time. If there's anything you'd like to say to Ryo-chan, do so. You can say things to each other, too, not just to Ryo-chan. One by one, standing in the middle."

It was not only the first time they had ever eaten dried squid at Tomoe, but the first time Ryo-chan had sat down with them, and the first time they had seen Ryo-chan sipping saké.

One after the other the children stood up, facing Ryo-chan, and spoke to him. The first children just told him to take care of himself and not get sick. Then Migita, who was in Totto-chan's class, said, "Next time I go home to the country I'll bring you all back some funeral dumplings."

Everyone laughed. It was well over a year since Migita first told them about the dumplings he had once had at a funeral and how good they were. Whenever the opportunity arose, he promised to bring them some, but he never did it.

When the headmaster heard Migita mention funeral dumplings, it gave him quite a start. Normally it would

れる」、と約束してたんだけど、一度も、持ってきてくれたことがないからだった）

校長先生は、初め、この右田君の「葬式まんじゅう」という言葉を聞いたときは、（どきっ !!）とした。ふつうなら、縁起（えんぎ）が、悪い言葉だから。でも、右田君が、実に無邪気に、「みんなに、おいしいものを喰べさせたい」という気持ちを表わしているのだから、と、一緒に笑った。良ちゃんも、大笑いした。良ちゃんも、もう、ずーっと、「持って来てやる」、と、右田君から、いわれていたからだった。

大栄君は、

「僕は、日本一の園芸家になります」

と、約束した。大栄君は、等々力（とどろき）にある、物凄（ものすご）く、大きい園芸家の子供だった。青木恵子ちゃんは、だまって立つと、いつものように、恥ずかしそうに笑って、だまって、おじぎをして、席にもどった。トットちゃんは、出しゃばって、まん中にいくと、恵子ちゃんの、おじぎに、つけ足した。

「恵子ちゃん家（ち）の、ニワトリ、空を、とぶんでーす。私は、この間、見ましたよ！」

天寺（あまでら）君がいった。

「ケガした猫や、犬がいたら、僕のところへ持ってきてね。なおして、あげるから」

高橋君は、机の下を、あっ！　という間に、くぐって、まん中に立つと、元気にいった。

「良ちゃん、ありがとう。いろんなこと、全部、ありがとう」

税所（さいしょ）愛子さんは、

「良ちゃん、いつか、ころんだとき、包帯（ほうたい）してくださって、ありがとう。忘れません」

といった。税所さんは、日露（にちろ）戦争で有名な、東郷元帥（とうごうげんすい）が大叔父（おおおじ）さまにあたり、また、明治時代の、おうたどころの歌人として知

have been considered bad luck to mention funeral dumplings at such a time. But Migita said it so innocently, just wanting to share with his friends something that tasted so good, that the headmaster laughed with the others. Ryo-chan laughed heartily, too. After all, Migita had been telling him for ages that he would bring him some.

Then Oe got up and promised Ryo-chan that he was going to become the best horticulturist in Japan. Oe was the son of the proprietor of an enormous nursery garden in Todoroki. Keiko Aoki got up next and said nothing. She just giggled shyly, as usual, and bowed, and went back to her seat. Whereupon Totto-chan rushed forward and said for her, "The chickens at Keiko-chan's can fly! I saw them the other day!"

Then Amadera spoke. "If you find any injured cats or dogs," he said, "bring them to me and I'll fix them up."

Takahashi was so small he crawled under his desk to get to the center of the circle and was there as quick as a wink. He said in a cheerful voice, "Thank you Ryo-chan. Thank you for everything. For all sorts of things."

Aiko Saisho stood up next. She said, "Ryo-chan, thank you for bandaging me up that time I fell down. I'll never forget." Aiko Saisho's great-uncle was the famous Admiral Togo of the Russo-Japanese War, and Atsuko Saisho, another relative of hers, was a celebrated poetess at Emperor Meiji's court. But Aiko never mentioned them.

られた税所敦子の親戚でもあった。(でも、税所さんは、自分で、そういうことを口に出すことは、一度もなかった)

ミヨちゃんは、校長先生の娘だから、一番、良ちゃんと、親しい間柄だった。そのせいか、涙が、目に、いっぱいになった。

「気をつけて行ってね、良ちゃん。手紙、書くわね」

トットちゃんは、あんまりたくさん、いいたいことがあって、困った。でも、これに決めた。

「良ちゃんが行っちゃっても、私たちは、毎日、サワカイ、やりまーす!!」

校長先生も良ちゃんも笑った。みんなも、トットちゃんまで笑った。

でも、このトットちゃんのいった事は、次の日から、本当になった。みんなは、ひまがあると、グループになって、「サワカイごっこ」を始めた。スルメのかわりに、木の皮などを、しゃぶりながら、お酒のつもりの、お水の入ったグラスを、チビチビやりながら、

「葬式まんじゅう、持ってくるからね」

とかいっては、笑って、自分たちの気持ちを発表しあった。たべものがなくても、サワカイは、楽しかった。

この「サワカイ」は、良ちゃんが、トモエに残してくれた、すばらしい贈りものだった。そして、そのときは、みんなが考えてもいなかったことだけど、これが、実は、そのあと、みんなが、別れ別れになってしまう前の、トモエでの最後の、心の通いあう、楽しい、お遊びだったのだ。

良ちゃんは、東横線に乗って、出発した。

やさしい良ちゃんと入れ違いに、アメリカの飛行機が、とうとう、東京の空に現われて、毎日、爆弾を、落としはじめた。

Miyo-chan, the headmaster's daughter, knew Ryo-chan the best. Her eyes were full of tears. "Take care of yourself, won't you, Ryo-chan. Let's write to each other."

Totto-chan had so many things she wanted to say she didn't know where to begin. So she just said, "Even though you're gone, Ryo-chan, we'll have a tea party every day."

The headmaster laughed, and so did Ryo-chan. All the children laughed, too, even Totto-chan herself.

But Totto-chan's words came true the very next day. Whenever there was time the children would form a group and play "tea party." Instead of dried squid, they would suck things like tree bark, and they sipped glasses of water instead of tea, sometimes pretending it was saké. Someone would say, "I'll bring you some funeral dumplings," and they'd all laugh. Then they'd talk and tell each other their thoughts. Even though there wasn't anything to eat, the "tea parties" were fun.

The "tea party" was a wonderful farewell gift that Ryo-chan left the children. And although none of them had the faintest idea then, it was in fact the last game they were to play at Tomoe before the children parted and went their separate ways.

Ryo-chan went off on the Toyoko train. His departure coincided with the arrival of the American airplanes. They finally appeared in the skies above Tokyo and began dropping bombs every day.

さよなら、さよなら

トモエが焼けた。

それは、夜のことだった。学校に続いている、校長先生の家にいたミヨちゃんや、お姉さんのみさちゃんや、ミヨちゃんのお母さんは、九品仏（くほんぶつ）の池のそばの、トモエの農園に逃げて、無事だった。

B29の飛行機から、焼夷弾（しょういだん）は、いくつも、いくつも、トモエの、電車の校舎の上に落ちた。

校長先生の夢だった学校は、いま、炎に包まれていた。先生が何よりも愛した子供たちの笑い声や、歌声のかわりに、学校は、恐ろしい音をたてて、くずれていく。もう、手のつけようもないくらい、その火は、学校を焼いた。自由が丘の、あっちこっちにも、火の手が、あがった。

その中で、校長先生は、通りに立って、トモエの焼けるのを、じーっと、見ていた。いつものように、少しヨレヨレの、でも、黒の三（み）つ揃（ぞろ）いだった。上着のポケットに、両手をつっこんだ、いつもの形だった。校長先生は、火を見ながら、そばに立っている息子の、大学生の巴（ともえ）さんに、いった。

「おい、今度は、どんな学校、作ろうか?」

巴さんは、びっくりして、小林先生の言葉を聞いた。

小林先生の子供に対する愛情、教育に対する情熱は、学校を、いま包んでいる炎より、ずーっと大きかった。先生は、元気だった。

その頃、トットちゃんは、満員の疎開（そかい）列車の中で、大人にはさまれながら、寝ていた。汽車は、東北に、むかっていた。トットちゃんは、別れぎわに、先生が、いったこと、

「また逢おうな！」

それから、いつも、いつも、いい続けてくださった、

「君は、本当は、いい子なんだよ」

Sayonara, Sayonara!

Tomoe burned down. It happened at night. Miyo-chan, her sister Misa-chan, and their mother—who all lived in the house adjoining the school—fled to the Tomoe farm by the pond at Kuhonbutsu Temple and were safe.

Lots of incendiary bombs dropped by the B29 bombers fell on the railroad cars that served as school-rooms.

The school that had been the headmaster's dream was enveloped in flames. Instead of the sounds he loved so much of children laughing and children singing, the school was collapsing with a fearful noise. The fire, impossible to quench, burned it down to the ground. Fires blazed up all over Jiyugaoka.

In the midst of it all, the headmaster stood in the road and watched Tomoe burn. He was dressed, as usual, in his rather shabby black three-piece suit. He stood with both hands in his jacket pockets.

"What kind of school shall we build next?" he asked his university-student son Tomoe, who stood beside him. Tomoe listened to him dumbfounded.

Mr. Kobayashi's love for children and his passion for teaching were stronger than the flames now enveloping the school. The headmaster was cheerful.

Totto-chan was lying down in a crowded evacuation train, squeezed in amongst adults. The train was headed northeast. As she looked out of the window at the darkness outside, she thought of the headmaster's

（……このことを忘れないようにしましょう）

と、暗い窓の外を見ながら、考えた。そして、

（いつか、また、すぐ小林先生に逢えるんだから）

と安心して、寝たのだった。

汽車は、闇(やみ)の中を、不安な人たちをのせ、音をたてて、走っていた。

parting words, "We'll meet again!" and the words he used to say to her time and time again, "You're really a good girl, you know." She didn't want to forget those words. Safe in the thought that soon she would see Mr. Kobayashi again, she fell asleep.

The train rumbled along in the darkness with its load of anxious passengers.

あとがき

トモエ学園と小林宗作先生のことを書く、というのは、長い間、もっとも、私がしたいと思っていたことの、ひとつでした。

この中に書いたことは、どれも作りものじゃなく、実際にあったことでした。そして、ありがたいことに、私は、いろんなことを、忘れていませんでした。それを、書いておきたい、ということと、もうひとつ、この本の「約束」の章で、私は「大きくなったら、トモエの先生になってあげる」、と小林先生と約束をしました。それなのに、その約束を実行しませんでした。ですから、せめて、こういう小林先生という人がいて、どんなに子供に対して深い愛情を持っていたか、子供たちを、どんな風に教育したか、ということを、具体的に、お伝えしなくちゃ、と思ったんです。

悲しいことに、小林先生は、昭和三十八年に亡くなってしまいました。生きてらしたら、もっともっと、いろんなこと、教えて頂けるのに、と残念です。

そして、こうやって、書きだしてみますと、若い頃は、ただ、楽しい思い出として残っていたトモエが、いまごろになって、
「ああ、小林先生は、こういうつもりだったんだ！」とか、
「先生は、こんなことまで考えていて下さったのか……」、とわかってきて、そのたびに、驚き、感動し、ありがたく思えるのです。

私のことでいえば、「君は本当はいい子なんだよ」、といい続けて下さった、この言葉が、どんなに、私の、これまでを支(ささ)えてく

Postscript

To write about Tomoe and its headmaster Sosaku Kobayashi is one of the things I have most wanted to do for a long time.

I have invented none of the episodes. They all really happened and, thankfully, I have remembered quite a few of them. Besides writing them down, I wanted to make amends for a broken pledge. As described in "The Promise," I vowed that I would teach at Tomoe when I grew up. But I did not keep that promise. So I want to tell what sort of man Mr. Kobayashi was, his great love for children, and how he set about educating them. Sadly, Mr. Kobayashi died in 1963. If he were alive today he could have told me much more.

As I write I realize how many episodes that just seem happy childhood memories to me were, in fact, activities carefully thought out by him to achieve certain results. "So that's what Mr. Kobayashi must have had in mind," I find myself thinking. Or, "Fancy him even thinking about that." With each discovery I make, I am amazed—and deeply moved and grateful.

In my own case, I have been immeasurably sustained by the way he kept saying to me, "You're really a good

れたか、計りしれません。もし、トモエに入ることがなく、小林先生にも逢わなかったら、私は、恐らく、なにをしても、「悪い子」、というレッテルを貼られ、コンプレックスにとらわれ、どうしていいかわからないままの、大人になっていた、と思います。

トモエは、昭和二十年の東京大空襲のときに焼けました。本当に、小林先生の私財で作った学校でした。ですから、再興には、時間が、かかりました。戦後、先生は、まず焼跡で幼稚園を始め、同時に、国立音大の保育科（現在の幼児教育科）を創るのに協力したり、また、国立音大でリトミックを教え、ここに小学校が出来るときも、手伝いました。でも、先生の夢、理想の、ご自分の小学校を再び作る前に、六十九歳で、亡くなってしまったのでした。

昔、トモエのあった場所は、東横線の自由が丘の駅から歩いて三分、現在は、ピーコック・スーパーストアと、その駐車場になっています。この前、なつかしくて、まったく昔の面影のないことは、わかっていましたが、車で行って、いま駐車場になっているあたり……電車の教室や、運動場だったとこ……を見ようと徐行しました。そしたら、駐車場のおじさんが、私の車を見て、「満車！　満車！　ダメ！　ダメ!!」と、叫びました。私は、
「いいえ、私の小学校のことを考えていたんです」、といいたかったけど、そんなこと、誰にもわかって頂けることじゃないから、と、いそいで、そこを離れました。でも、なんだか急に悲しくなって、走り出した車の中で、涙がポロポロとこぼれたのでした。

日本にも、たくさんの、いい教育者のかたは、いらっしゃると思います。みなさん、理想も愛情も、夢も、お持ちと思いますが、それを実際のものとするのが、どんなに難かしいか、私にも、よくわかります。小林先生にしても、このトモエ学園を始める前に、何年も何年も研究し、完全なものとして学校を始めたのが、昭和

girl, you know." Had I not entered Tomoe and never met Mr. Kobayashi, I would probably have been labeled "a bad girl," becoming complex-ridden and confused.

Tomoe was destroyed by fire in the Tokyo air raids in 1945. Mr. Kobayashi had built the school with his own money, so reestablishing it took time. After the war, he started a kindergarten on the old site, while helping to establish what is now the Child Education Department of Kunitachi College of Music. He also taught eurythmics there and assisted in the establishment of Kunitachi Elementary School. He died, aged sixty-nine, before he could restart his ideal school.

Tomoe Gakuen was a three-minute walk from Jiyugaoka Station on the Toyoko Line. The site is now occupied by the Peacock supermarket. I went there the other day out of nostalgia, knowing nothing was left of the school or its grounds. I drove slowly past the parking lot, where the railroad-car classrooms and playground used to be. The man in charge called out, "You can't come in. We're full!" "I don't want to park," I felt like saying, "I'm just evoking memories." But he would not have understood. So sadly I went on, tears rolling down my cheeks as I sped away.

I am sure the world over there are fine educators with high ideals and a great love for children who dream of setting up ideal schools. And I know how difficult it must be to realize this dream. It took Mr. Kobayashi years of study before starting Tomoe in 1937 and it burned down in 1945, so its existence was very brief.

十二年。焼けたのが、二十年ですから、本当に短い期間でした。

でも、私のいた頃が、先生にとって、最も情熱が強く、先生のやりたいことが花開いた瞬間だったようで、その点、幸福だと思っています。でも、戦争さえなければ、どんなに沢山の生徒が、小林先生の手から世の中に出て行ったか、と思うと、勿体ない、と、悲しい気持です。

小林先生の教育方針は、この本にも書きましたが、常に、「どんな子も、生まれたときには、いい性質を持っている。それが大きくなる間に、いろいろな、まわりの環境とか、大人たちの影響で、スポイルされてしまう。だから、早く、この『いい性質』を見つけて、それをのばしていき、個性のある人間にしていこう」というのでした。

また、先生は、自然が好きでした。子供たちの性格も、出来るだけ自然であること、と考えてらしたようですが、実際の自然も好きで、末娘のミヨちゃんの話によると、小さいとき、いつも、

「自然の中のリズムを見つけよう」

という先生に連れられて散歩に出かけたのだそうです。先生は、そういうとき、いつも、大きな木のところに行って、風があたったときの木の葉や、木の枝の揺れかた、そして、一つの枝を見ると、次は、その上の枝と、その葉っぱ。また、みきとの関係。風の強さと弱さで、葉っぱの揺れかたは、どんなに違うか……。そういう事を、じーっと観察し、風が吹かなければ、いつまでも、上をむいて、立っていた、ということでした。これは、木だけではなく、川でも同じことで、近くの多摩(たま)川に出かけては、川の流れを見て、飽きることがなかったそうです。

それにしても、あの戦争中、こんな自由な小学校を、なぜ、文部省や、国が許したのか、と疑問をお持ちのかたも、いらっしゃると思います。くわしいことは、いまになっては、わかりませんが、確かなのは、なんといっても小林先生が、宣伝ぎらい、今で

I like to believe that the period I was there was when Mr. Kobayashi's enthusiasm was at its height and his schemes in full flower. But when I think how many children could have come under his care had there been no war, I am saddened at the waste.

I have tried to describe Mr. Kobayashi's educational methods in this book. He believed all children are born with an innate good nature, which can be easily damaged by their environment and the wrong adult influences. His aim was to uncover their "good nature" and develop it, so that the children would grow into people with individuality.

Mr. Kobayashi valued naturalness and wanted to let children's characters develop as naturally as possible. He loved nature, too. His younger daughter, Miyo-chan, told me her father took her for walks when she was small, saying, "Let's go and look for the rhythms in nature."

He would lead her to a large tree and show her how the leaves and branches swayed in the breeze; he would point out the relationship between the leaves, branches, and trunk; and how the swaying differed when the wind was strong or weak. They would stand still and observe things like that, and if there was no wind, they would wait patiently, with upturned faces, for the slightest zephyr. They observed not only the wind, but rivers, too. They used to go to the nearby Tama River and watch the water flowing. They never tired of doing things like that, she told me.

いうマスコミ嫌い、ということで、戦前でも、一度も、学校の写真を撮らせるとか、「変った学校ですよ」、と宣伝することがありませんでした。そのおかげで、この小さい、全校生で五十人足らず、という小学校が、誰の目に触れることもなく、継続できたのではないでしょうか。

私たち、トモエの生徒だったみんなは、学年に関係なく、毎年、今でも、十一月三日＝あの素晴しい運動会だった思い出の日＝に、九品仏(くほんぶつ)のお寺のお部屋を拝借して集り、楽しい一日を過します。もう、みんな四十歳をすぎ、やがて五十歳になろう、という子供づれが、「サッコちゃん」とか、「大栄(おおえ)君！」とかいって、昔とかわらない、おつきあいをしているのです。これも、小林先生が、私たちに残して下さった贈りものです。

私が、前の小学校を退学になったのも、本当のことで、私は、あまり憶(おぼ)えていなかったのですが、チンドン屋さんのこととか、机のフタのことなどは、あとで母が話してくれた事でした。それでも私は、「本当かなあ？　私は、そんなに、ひどい子だって思ってなかったけど」、と、内心で思っていました。ところが、今から五年くらい前に、テレビ朝日の「奈良和モーニングショウ」で、御対面、というのがあり、「何方(どなた)か？」と思いましたら、その退学になった学校の、私と同じ一年生の、隣りのクラスの受持ちの女の先生が、おいで下さったのです。その先生の話を伺(うかが)って、私は、びっくりしました。その先生の話は、こうでした。

「徹子さんは、隣りのクラスの生徒さんでした。授業中、私は職員室に用事があることがあり、生徒に自習をさせて、廊下に出ますと、ほとんど毎日、あなたが廊下に立たされているんです。そして、私が通りかかりますと、徹子さんは、私を呼び止めて、

『先生、私、立たされているんですけど、どうして？』とか、

『私は、どんな悪いことをしたの？』とか、

『先生はチンドン屋さん嫌(きら)い？』とか話しかけて来るので、困っ

Readers may wonder how the authorities in wartime allowed such a free elementary school to exist. Mr. Kobayashi disliked the press, and even before the war did not allow photographs or any publicity about its unconventionality. That may have been one reason this small school of under fifty pupils escaped notice and managed to continue.

Every November third—the day of those wonderful Sports Days—the pupils of Tomoe, regardless of age, get together in a room in Kuhonbutsu Temple for a happy reunion. Although we are nearing fifty, some with grown children, we still call each other by our nicknames just as in the old days. These reunions are one of the many happy legacies Mr. Kobayashi left us.

It is true that I was expelled from my first elementary school. I do not remember much about it. My mother told me about the street musicians and the desk. I found it hard to believe I had been expelled. Was I really as naughty as all that? However, five years ago on a morning television show, I met someone who had known me at that time: the homeroom teacher of the class next to mine. I was dumbfounded at what she told me.

"When I had to go to the faculty room during class," she said, I usually found you standing in the corridor for some misdemeanor. As I went past, you always stopped me and asked why you'd been made to stand out there, and what you had done wrong. 'Don't you like street musicians?' you asked me once. I never knew how to deal with you, so finally, even if I wanted to go to the

てしまうんです。ですから、しまいには、職員室に用事があっても、戸を開けて見て、徹子さんが立たされていると、出るのをやめてしまいました。あなたの受持ちの先生も、よく職員室で、私に、『どうして、ああなんでしょう』、と話してらっしゃいましたよ。そんなわけで、あなたが後年テレビにお出になったとき、すぐ、お名前でわかりました。あんな昔のことなのに、あなたの一年生の頃のことは、はっきりと、おぼえていましたから……」

（立たされていた?）私は、全く自分でおぼえていなかったことなので、びっくりしましたが、同時に、朝早いテレビなのに出て来て下さった、白髪で優しそうな先生の若い姿と、廊下で立たされているのにもかかわらず、なお、「知りたがりのテツコちゃん」ぶりを発揮している自分の姿を想像し、おかしくもあり、同時に、やはり退学は、本当だったのだ、と納得したのでした。

ここで私は、私の母に、心からの感謝を伝えたいと思います。それは、「退学になった」、という事実を、私が二十歳すぎまで話さないでくれた、という事です。

二十歳を過ぎた、ある日、母が、

「あのとき、どうして小学校かわったか、知ってる?」と聞きました。私が、

「ううん?」というと、母は、「本当は退学になったのよ」、と軽い感じで言いました。

もし、あの一年生のとき、

「どうするの?　あなた、もう退学になっちゃって！　次の学校に入ったって、もし、また退学にでもなったら、もう行くところなんか、ありませんからね!!」

もし、こんな風に母にいわれたとしたら、私は、どんなに、みじめな、オドオドした気持で、トモエの門を、あの初めての日に、くぐった事でしょう。そしたら、あの、根の生（は）えた門も、電車の教室も、あんなに、楽しくは見えなかったに違いありません。こ

faculty room I would peep out first, and if you were in the corridor I avoided going. Your homeroom teacher often talked about you to me in the faculty room. 'I wonder why she's like that,' she would say. When you started appearing on television, I recognized your name immediately. It was a long time ago, but I remember you distinctly when you were in first grade."

Was I made to stand outside in the corridor? I hadn't remembered that and was surprised. It was this youthful-looking, gray-haired teacher with a kindly face, who had taken the trouble to come to an early morning television show, who finally convinced me that I really had been expelled.

I would like to express my heartfelt gratitude to my mother for not having told me until after my twentieth birthday.

"Do you know why you changed elementary schools?" she asked me one day. When I said no, she went on, quite nonchalantly, "You were expelled."

She might have said at the time, "What's going to become of you? You've already been expelled from one school. If they expel you from the next, where will you go?"

If Mother had, how wretched and nervous I would have felt as I entered the gate of Tomoe Gakuen on my first day there. That gate with roots and those railroad-car classrooms would not have looked nearly so delightful. How lucky I was to have a mother like mine.

With the war on, only a few photographs were taken

ういう母に育てられた事も私は幸せでした。

戦争中なので、あまりトモエの写真はありません。少しある中で面白いのは、卒業式の写真です。講堂の正面の階段のところで、たいがい卒業生は写真を写したのですが、

「写真だ！　写真だ！」ということで卒業生が並ぶと、在校生も一緒に写りたがって、あっちからも、こっちからも顔を出したので、出来上った写真は、誰が本当の卒業生かわからず、みんなで集っては、

「これは、誰のクラスの卒業のときのだ」、と、研究するありさまです。でも、小林先生は、そういうとき、なにもおっしゃいませんでした。卒業式という決まった写真より、みんなが生き生きと、自由に写っているほうがいい、と考えていらしたのでしょうか。そして、今になれば、これほど、トモエらしい写真はない、と思えます。

トモエのことで書くことは、まだ沢山ありました。でも、とにかく、こういう、トットちゃんみたいな女の子でも、まわりの大人のやりかたによって、なんとか、みんなとやっていける人間になれる、という事を知って頂けたら、と思っているのです。

そして、もし、今でもトモエがあったら、「登校拒否する子なんて、一人もいないだろうな」、と考えます。だって、トモエでは、みんな学校が終っても、放課後、家に帰りたくないぐらいだったんですから。そして、また、次の朝は、早く学校に行きたくて、待ち切れないくらいだったんです。トモエというのは、そういう学校でした。

小林宗作先生の略歴です。

明治二十六年六月十八日、群馬県吾妻（あがつま）郡に生まれる。小さい時から音楽が好きで、榛名（はるな）山の見える家の前の川のほとりで、いつも、指揮棒を振って遊んでいたという。六人兄姉の豊かではない

at Tomoe. Among them the graduation photographs are the nicest. The graduating class usually had its photograph taken on the steps in front of the Assembly Hall, but when the graduates started lining up with shouts of, "Picture, picture!" other children would want to get in it, too, so it is impossible to tell who was graduating. We have animated discussions on the subject at our reunions. Mr. Kobayashi never spoke on these picture-taking occasions. Perhaps he thought it better to have a lively photograph of us all than a formal graduation picture. Looking at them now, they are very representative of Tomoe.

I could have written much more about Tomoe. But I shall be content if people realize how even a little girl like Totto-chan, given the right kind of adult influence, can learn to get along with others.

I am quite sure that if there were schools now like Tomoe, there would be less of the violence we hear so much of today and fewer school dropouts. At Tomoe nobody wanted to go home when school was over. And in the morning we could hardly wait to get there. It was that kind of school.

Sosaku Kobayashi, the man who had the inspiration and vision to set up this wonderful school, was born on June 18, 1893, in the country northwest of Tokyo. Nature and music were his passions, and as a child he would stand on the bank of the river near his home, with Mount Haruna in the distance, and pretend the gushing waters

農家の末っ子だったので、小学校を卒業すると、すぐ代用教員となり、検定試験で教員の免許をとる。(小学校を出ただけで、検定試験に受かる、というのは、よほど優秀だったに違いないと思います。)上京。牛込小学校の先生となるかたわら、音楽の勉強をし、念願だった東京音楽学校（今の芸大）の師範科に入学。卒業後、成蹊小学校の音楽教師になる。この学校の創立者、中村春二の教育方針が、小林先生に大きな影響をあたえる。中村春二は素晴しい人で、「教育は、どうしても小学校から、やらなければ！」、という考えを持っていて、生徒の数は、絶対に一クラス多くても三十人。そして自由な教育、子供の個性尊重に徹する教育方針を、うち出した。例えば、勉強は午前中で終り、午後は散歩とか、植物採集、写生、先生の話を聞く、歌をうたう、といったように、後年、トモエで小林先生が実行したような授業方法だった。

この学校で、小林先生は、生徒のために、子供のためのオペレッタを作った。それを、このユニークな学校の創立者でもあり、その頃、山田耕筰など、数多くの芸術家を財政の面で援助していた、三菱の財閥、岩崎小弥太男爵（エリザベス・サンダース・ホームの沢田美樹さんのお父様のいとこ）が見て感動し、ヨーロッパでの教育を視察するための費用を援助しよう、という事になった。丁度そのころ、音楽教育、児童教育に、いろいろ悩みを持っていた小林先生は、よろこんでこの申し出を受け、第一回のヨーロッパ留学に出発する。大正十二年、先生が三十歳のときでした。

世界中に大きな影響をあたえたダルクローズのパリの学校で直接ダルクローズから学び、その他、いろいろの学校などを見て歩き、二年後、日本に帰ってくる。帰るとすぐ、小林先生の幼児教育に全面的に共鳴した、小原国芳と、成城幼稚園を創る。

この幼稚園で小林先生は、「子供を先生の計画に、はめるな。自然の中に放り出しておけ。先生の計画より子供の夢のほうが、ずっと大きい」と、保育の先生にいいわたし、小林先生は、従来の

were an orchestra, which he would "conduct."

He was the youngest son of six children in a rather poor farming family and had to work as an assistant schoolteacher after an elementary education. To obtain the necessary certificate, however, was quite a feat for a boy that age, and it showed exceptional talent. Soon he got a position at an elementary school in Tokyo, and he combined teaching with music studies, which finally enabled him to carry out his cherished ambition and enter the Music Education Department of Japan's foremost conservatory of music—now the Tokyo University of Fine Arts and Music. On graduation, he became music instructor at Seikei Elementary School, founded by Haruji Nakamura, a wonderful man who believed a child's elementary education was the most important. He kept classes small with a free curriculum to bring out the child's individuality and promote self-respect. Study was done in the mornings. Afternoons were devoted to walks, plant collecting, sketching, singing, and listening to discourses by the headmaster. Mr. Kobayashi was greatly influenced by his methods and instituted a similar kind of curriculum at Tomoe.

While teaching music there, Mr. Kobayashi wrote a children's operetta for the students to perform. The operetta impressed the industrialist Baron Iwasaki, whose family founded the giant business enterprise Mitsubishi. Baron Iwasaki, cousin of the father of Miki Sawada, who founded the Elizabeth Sanders Home, was a patron of the arts—helping Kosçak Yamada,

幼稚園と全くちがった幼稚園を、ここに作った。

昭和五年、小林先生は、二回目のヨーロッパに出発する。実際に教えてみて、もう一度、リトミックを勉強する必要があると思ったので、ダルクローズのところへ再び。それから、いろいろ視察し、本格的に自分の学校を創る事を決め、一年後に帰国。

昭和十二年、トモエ幼稚園とトモエ学園（小学校）を創立する。日本リトミック協会も設立した。

小林先生を、「リトミックを日本に普及させた人」として知っている人、また研究している人は多いけど、子供の教育の具体的な例を知っている人、となると、当時の私たちのほか、ほんの少しになりました。小林先生は、先にも書きましたが、トモエの焼けたあと、国立（くにたち）幼稚園の園長とか国立（くにたち）音大の講師など、いろいろなさいましたが、自分流の、あのトモエのような小学校を創る前に、亡くなってしまったのです。空襲で焼けるトモエを見ながら、「今度は、どんな学校を作ろうか」と、おっしゃった先生の情熱が、再び、よみがえる前に。

いま私が出演しているテレビ朝日の「徹子の部屋」のチーフ・プロデューサーは、佐野和彦さんといいますが、このかたは、「小林宗作という素晴しい教育者がいた」という事を聞き、この十年間、研究をしてきました。私は佐野さんとお知り合いになって、かれこれ十年になります。でも、その間、私は、佐野さんが小林先生を調べてる事は知らなかったし、佐野さんも、私が「素晴しい校長先生に育ててもらった」という事は知っていましたが、まさか、それが小林先生とは、夢にも思っていなかったんです。それが、この「トットちゃん」を書き始めたとき、突然わかって、佐野さんは、とび上って、よろこびました。「こんな身近なところに、長い間、探していた事を知ってる人がいた……」。

佐野さんが小林先生の事を、本当に調べよう、と思ったきっかけは、小林先生がリトミックを教えるときに子供のためにピアノ

doyen of Japanese composers, as well as giving financial support to the school. The baron offered to send Mr. Kobayashi to Europe to study educational methods.

Mr. Kobayashi spent two years in Europe, from 1922 to 1924, visiting schools and studying eurythmics with Emile Jaques-Dalcroze in Paris. On his return, he established Seijo Kindergarten with Kuniyoshi Obara. Mr. Kobayashi used to tell the kindergarten teachers not to try and fit the children into preconceived molds. "Leave them to nature," he would say. "Don't cramp their ambitions. Their dreams are bigger than yours." There had never been a kindergarten like it in Japan.

In 1930, Mr. Kobayashi set off for Europe for a further year of study with Dalcroze, traveling around and making observations, and decided to start his own school on returning to Japan.

Besides starting Tomoe Gakuen in 1937, he also established the Japan Eurythmics Association. Most people remember him for introducing eurythmics to Japan and for his work at Kunitachi College of Music after the war. There are very few of us left who directly experienced his teaching, and it is a tragedy that he died before establishing another school like Tomoe. As it burned, he already envisaged a better school. "What kind of school shall we build next?" he asked, in high spirits, undaunted by the commotion around him.

When I began writing this book, I was amazed to find that the producer of "Tetsuko's Room," my daily television interview program—a producer I had worked

の伴奏（ばんそう）をした女の人に、逢ったときでした。その女の人は、小林先生から、こういう風にいわれたと、佐野さんにいいました。

「君、子供は、そんな風には歩かないんだよ」つまり、子供の呼吸が、わかっていない！　と、小林先生は注意したのです。このひとことで、佐野さんは、小林先生の研究を始めたのです。佐野さんの繊細（せんさい）な感覚とリサーチで、小林先生の、もっと、くわしいことがわかるといい、と、私は楽しみにしています。

「窓ぎわのトットちゃん」は、講談社の「若い女性」に、一九七九年の二月から一九八〇年十二月まで二年間、連載したものを、まとめて頂いたものです。

「窓ぎわ」という題名にしたのは、これを書き始めた頃、「窓ぎわ族」という言葉が、流行しました。なんとなく疎外されている。もはや第一線ではない。そういう響きが、そこにありました。私はチンドン屋さんを待つために、いつも窓ぎわにいました。どことなく疎外感も、初めの学校では感じていました。そんなわけで、こういう題名にしたのです。

　この本の美しく可愛い絵の作者、いわさきちひろさんに感謝します。残念なことに、ちひろさんは、昭和四十九年にお亡くなりになりました。でも、約七千点の素晴しい絵を、お残しになりました。御存知のように、ちひろさんは、子供の絵の天才でした。恐らく世界中でも、こんなに生き生きと子供を描く画家は、いないと思います。子供なら、どんなポーズでも、また、六ヵ月の赤ちゃんと九ヵ月の赤ちゃんを、ちひろさんは描きわけられたのです。いつも子供の味方、子供の幸福を願っていた、ちひろさんの絵を、このトモエの本を書くときに使わせて頂きたい、これは、私の夢でした。それが実現して、こんなにうれしい事はありません。いわさきちひろ絵本美術館（私も館長をしている）の副館長であるちひろさんの息子さんの松本猛さんと、奥さまの由理子さ

with for years—had been doing research on Mr. Kobayashi for a decade. He had never met the educator, but his interest was aroused by a woman who once played the piano for children's eurythmics classes. "Children don't walk like that, you know," Mr. Kobayashi had said, correcting her tempo, when she first began. Here was a man so attuned to children that he knew how they breathed and how they moved. I am hoping Kazuhiko Sano, my producer, will write his book soon to tell the world a great deal more about this remarkable man.

I had written about Tomoe as a series of articles for Kodansha's *Young Woman* magazine, which I did from February 1979 to December 1980.

I got the idea for the title from an expression popular then that referred to people being "over by the window," or relegated as second-rate. Although I used to stand at the window out of choice, hoping to see the street musicians, I truly felt "over by the window" at that first school—alienated and very much out in the cold. The title has these overtones, as well as one more—the window of happiness that finally opened for me at Tomoe.

Chihiro Iwasaki was a genius at depicting children, and I doubt if any other artist could draw children in as lively a way. She captured them in their myriad moods and attitudes and could differentiate between a baby of six and nine months. I am delighted to have been able to use her drawings for my book.

んに、そして、絵を使うことを、快く許して下さった、ちひろさんの御主人の松本善明さんにも、心からの感謝を、申しあげます。

トモエは、もうないけれど、いま皆様に読んで頂いた間だけでも、トモエが、そこに昔のように、姿を現わせるとしたら、こんなうれしいことはありません。本当にありがとうございました。

一九八一年

黒柳 徹子

Chihiro Iwasaki died in 1974. She left nearly seven thousand paintings, and I was privileged to see a great many of them through the kindness of her son, assistant curator of the museum, and his wife. My gratitude also to the artist's husband for permission to reproduce her work.

Tomoe is no longer. But if it lives for a little while in your imagination as you read this book, nothing could give me greater joy.

Tokyo, 1981

Tetsuko Kuroyanagi

いわさきちひろ・収録画初出一覧

2　『チャームサロン10』千趣会、1971年（逆版使用）
4　出典不明
6-7　『ママの心得』小学館、1967年（逆版使用）
9　出典不明
11　出典不明
16　『家庭の教育3・少年期』習作、1966年
17　出典不明
19　ヒゲタしゅうゆ広告、1970年
22　『遠い絵本』旭書房、1972年
28　『となりにきたこ』至光社、1970年
29　『子どものしあわせ』草土文化、1967年
39　出典不明
51　『あかまんまとうげ』童心社、1972年
52　出典不明
58　『家庭の教育3・少年期』岩波書店、1966年
59　『家庭の教育3・少年期』岩波書店、1966年
60　『家庭の教育3・少年期』岩波書店、1966年
64　『家庭の教育2・幼年期』岩波書店、1966年
70　『ミセス』「育児駆出しの記」文化出版局、1972年
74　『母と生活』静岡教育出版社、1970年
78　『遠い絵本』旭書房、1972年
82　『子どものしあわせ』草土文化、1969年
88　『愛と規律の保育』童心社、1968年
93　『幼児の世界』世界文化社、1970年
96　『ミセス』「育児駆出しの記」文化出版局、1971年
106　『ひろば』至光社、1969年
114-5　『しょうがくしゃかい・1』日本書籍、1971年
122　ヒゲタしゅうゆ広告
134-5　『ひろば』至光社、1970年
136　出典不明
142　『随筆サンケイ』サンケイ新聞出版局、1970年
148　『赤い鳥名作集4』「鉛筆の心」中央公論社、1973年
150　『子どもを見る眼、保育を見る眼』全国社会福祉協議会、1969年
158　『母と生活』静岡教育出版社、1969年
171　『母と生活』静岡教育出版社、1969年
176　『家庭の教育3・少年期』岩波書店、1966年
194　『母と生活』静岡教育出版社、1968年

原画は、ちひろ美術館に保存されています。

★ いわさきちひろ絵本美術館
〒177　東京都練馬区下石神井4-7-2　☎(03) 3995-0820
交通　西武新宿線上井草下車、徒歩7分

★ 安曇野ちひろ美術館（1997年4月19日open）
〒399-85　長野県北安曇郡松川村西原　☎(0261) 62-0772
交通　ＪＲ大糸線信濃松川下車、車で5分

黒柳徹子 (Kuroyanagi Tetsuko)
女優、ユニセフ（国連児童基金/United Nations Children's Fund）親善大使。東京生まれ。1952年、東京音大声楽科卒業後、ＮＨＫ放送劇団に入る。以後、テレビ・舞台で活躍。1981年に刊行した『窓ぎわのトットちゃん』（本書の親本）は700万部の超ベストセラーに。『パンダと私』、『トットチャンネル』、『つば広の帽子をかぶって』（共著）など著書も多い。1984年にユニセフ親善大使となる。

ドロシー・ブリトン (Dorothy Britton)
作曲家、詩人、作家。横浜生まれの英国人。日英米三国で教育を受け、フランスのダリウス・ミオーに作曲を学ぶ。以後、日本に在住。音楽・文学など幅広く活躍。オペラ『夕鶴』の歌詞英訳をはじめ、著書に『日本の国立公園』（National Parks of Japan）、『日本の鶴』（The Japanese Crane）、訳書に『奥の細道』（A Haiku Journey）、『白旗の少女』（The Girl with the White Flag）など多数。

ベスト・オブ **窓ぎわのトットちゃん**
Best of Totto-chan: The Little Girl at the Window

発行日　1996年8月20日　第１刷発行

著　者　黒柳徹子
翻訳者　ドロシー・ブリトン
発行者　野間佐和子
発行所　講談社インターナショナル株式会社
〒112　東京都文京区音羽 1-17-14
電話　03-3944-6493（編集）
03-3944-6492（営業）
絵　いわさきちひろ
印刷所　大日本印刷株式会社
製本所　株式会社堅省堂

ISBN4-7700-2127-5

Bilingual Books 講談社バイリンガル・ブックス

既刊ラインナップ

英語で話す「日本」Q&A

Talking About Japan Q & A

講談社インターナショナル［編］

外国の人と話すとき、必ず出てくる話題は「日本」のこと。でも英語力よりも前に困るのは、日本について知らないことがいっぱいという事実です。モヤモヤの知識をスッキリさせてくれる「日本再発見」の書。

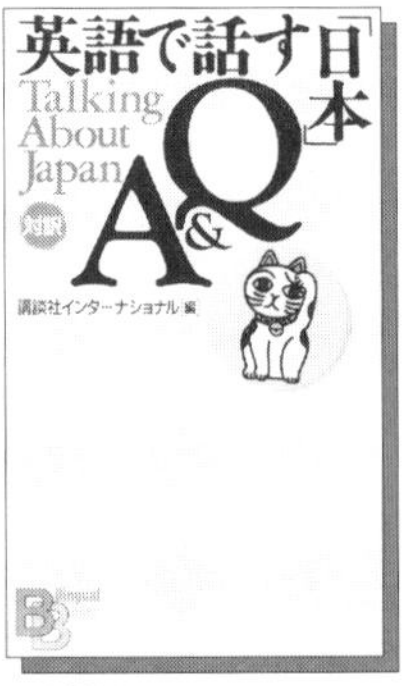

ISBN4-7700-2026-0

日米比較・冠婚葬祭のマナー

Do It Right: Japanese & American Social Etiquette

ジェームス・M・バーダマン／倫子・バーダマン［著］

アメリカでは結婚式や葬式はどのように行われるのか？　お祝いや香典は？……そしてアメリカの人たちも、日本の事情を知りたがります。これだけあればもう困らない。日米冠婚葬祭マニュアル、バイリンガル版。

ISBN4-7700-2025-2

英語で折り紙

Origami in English

山口　真［著］

たった一枚の紙から無数の造形が生まれ出る‥‥
外国の人たちは、その面白さに目を見張ります。
折るとき、英語で説明できるようにバイリンガル
にしました。ホームステイ、留学、海外駐在に必
携の一冊です。

ISBN4-7700-2027-9

英語で読む日本史

Japanese History: 11 Experts Reflect on the Past

「英文日本大事典」［編］

11人の超一流ジャパノロジストたちが英語で書き
下ろした日本全史。外国人の目から見た日本史は
どういうものか、また、日本の歴史事項を英語で
何と表現するのか。新しい視点が想像力をかき立
てます。

ISBN4-7700-2024-4

ベスト・オブ 宮沢賢治短編集

The Tales of Miyazawa Kenji

宮沢賢治［著］
ジョン・ベスター［訳］

『注文の多い料理店』『どんぐりと山猫』『祭の晩』
『鹿踊りのはじまり』『土神ときつね』『オツベルと
象』『毒もみの好きな署長さん』『セロ弾きのゴーシ
ュ』の代表作8編を精選。ジョン・ベスターの名訳
でどうぞ。

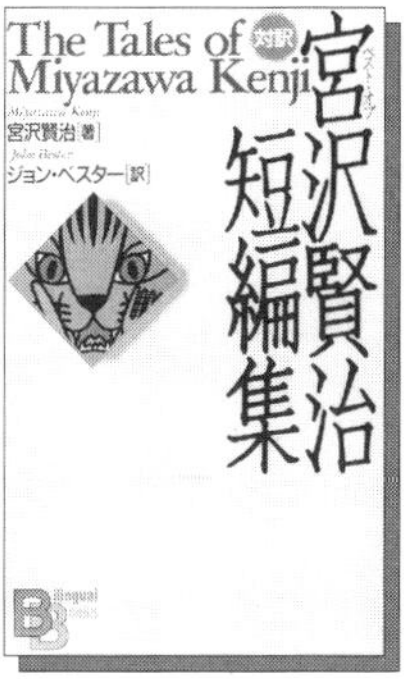

ISBN4-7700-2081-3

「Japan」クリッピング

Views of Japan from The Washington Post Newsroom

東郷茂彦［著］

アメリカの世論をリードするワシントン・ポストに書かれた「Japan」……政治、外交、経済、社会のジャンルで取り上げられた日本の姿を、国際ジャーナリストが解説し、その背後にある問題点を浮き彫りにする一冊。

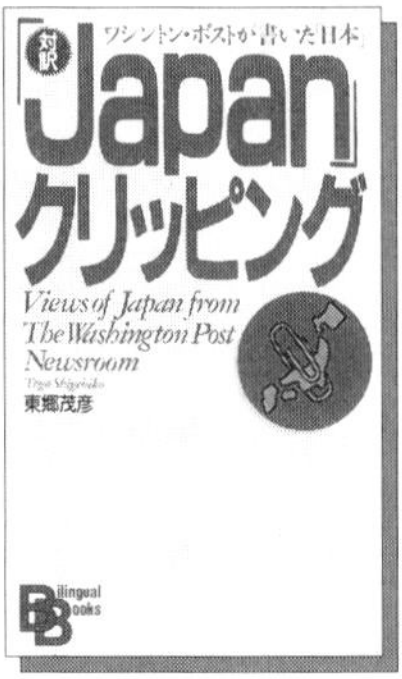

ISBN4-7700-2023-6

マザー・グース 愛される唄70選

Mother Goose: 70 Nursery Rhymes

谷川俊太郎［訳］
渡辺　茂［解説］

『マイ・フェア・レディー』や『お熱いのがお好き』という題名も、マザー・グースからの引用だったってこと、ご存じでしたか? 英米人にとって必須教養であるこの童謡集を、詩人・谷川俊太郎の名訳と共にお楽しみください。

ISBN4-7700-2078-3

ニッポン見聞録

Heisei Highs and Lows

トム・リード［著］

国際化の進む日本ですが、アメリカのジャーナリストが鋭い目と耳で浮き彫りにしたニッポンの姿は、驚くほど平穏で愛おしく、恥ずかしいくらい強欲で無知なものでした。トムが大好きな日本人へ贈る新・開国論。

ISBN4-7700-2092-9

ベスト・オブ 窓ぎわのトットちゃん

Best of Totto-chan:
The Little Girl at the Window

黒柳徹子［著］
ドロシー・ブリトン［訳］

小学校一年生にして“退学”になったトットちゃんは、転校先の校長先生に「君は本当はいい子なんだよ」と温かい言葉のシャワーに励まされます….
バイリンガル版で、あの空前の大ベストセラーの感動をもう一度！

ISBN4-7700-2127-5

銀河鉄道の夜

Night Train to the Stars

宮沢賢治［著］
ジョン・ベスター［訳］

賢治童話の中でも最も人気の高い『銀河鉄道の夜』は、賢治の宗教心と科学精神が反映された独特の世界——天空、自然、大地がみごとに描かれ、光と音と動きに満ち溢れています。ジョバンニと一緒に銀河を旅してみませんか。

ISBN4-7700-2131-3

英語で読んでも面白い！

1 楽しく読めて自然に英語が身に付くバイリンガル表記

2 実用から娯楽まで読者の興味に応える多彩なテーマ

3 重要単語、表現法が一目で分かる段落対応レイアウト